Certified Documentation Improvement Practitioner (CDIP) Exam Preparation

Second Edition

Sharon Easterling, MHA, RHIA, CCS, CDIP, CRC, FAHIMA

ISBN: 978-1-58426-909-0

eISBN: 978-1-58426-910-6

AHIMA Product No.: AB300622

AHIMA Staff:
Chelsea Brotherton, MA, Production Development Editor
Sarah Cybulski, MA, Assistant Editor
Megan Grennan, Director, Content Production and AHIMA Press
James Pinnick, Vice President, Content and Learning Solutions
Christine Scheid, Content Development Manager

Cover image: ©[copyright holder: person, place, etc.], [vendor name]

For more information, including updates, about AHIMA Press publications, visit http://www.ahima.org/education/press.

American Health Information Management Association
233 North Michigan Avenue, 21st Floor
Chicago, Illinois 60601-5809
ahima.org

Contents

About the Editor

Sharon Easterling, MHA, RHIA, CCS, CDIP, CRC, FAHIMA, is the CEO of Upskillz, LLC. Focusing on clinical documentation integrity and quality within documentation has been a focus for Sharon throughout her career. Beginning her health information (HI) journey more than 20 years ago, Ms. Easterling has extensive experience working in a variety of HI areas such as inpatient and outpatient coding, utilization review, CDI, recovery audits, as well as managing HI, quality initiatives, and coding departments. Ms. Easterling has had the unique background of exposure to both the acute and ambulatory settings throughout her career. Her past experience includes coding director and corporate assistant vice president at a large integrated health system and senior director of ambulatory clinical documentation improvement of a large medical group.

Her passion lies in documentation improvement and improving operational and financial performance for her clients. Her expertise in helping executive leadership set strategy for the future has made her a sought after resource. She has shared her experiences with other professionals through writing in many national publications as well as participation in the development of many American Health Information Management Association (AHIMA) Practice Briefs and educational sessions for NCHIMA, AHIMA, HFMA, and AAPC as well as other healthcare care entities. Ms. Easterling is a past AHIMA Member of the Board of Directors and past North Carolina Health Information Management Association (NCHIMA) President and Delegate for AHIMA. She is a past Chair and current member of the American College of Physician Advisors Advisory Board, RAC Monitor editorial board, and previous member of AHIMA Coding Community Practice Council, as well as the AHIMA CDI workgroup.

Acknowledgments

Documentation should be transparent. Thanks to you for taking the first step to see.

Thanks to all of you who impact me and others daily while on this HIM journey. Continue to grow our profession.

AHIMA Press wishes to thank Tina Bruce, MSHIM, MSHI, RHIA, CCS, CDIP, for her excellent technical review of this book.

About the CDIP Examination

Now more than ever, a strong, highly respected clinical documentation improvement (CDI) program can make a difference in achieving the goals of providers as they navigate population health, payor audits and constraints, interoperability, and other important initiatives aimed at improving the quality of healthcare. In response to industry demand, the Commission on Certification for Health Informatics and Information Management (CCHIIM) developed the CDIP credential.

Professionals earning the CDIP credential will:

- Be distinguished as knowledgeable and competent in clinical documentation in patient health records.
- Be positioned as leaders and role models in the health informatics and information management community.
- Demonstrate competency in capturing documentation necessary to fully communicate patients' health status and conditions.
- Help provide a strong base of expertise in the industry.

AHIMA certification can also help to:

- Improve earning potential.
- Increase opportunity for career advancement.
- Provide a forum to connect with colleagues.

As technology changes the way documentation is captured through the use of EHRs, AHIMA is leading the effort to ensure it is still clear, concise, and compliant. AHIMA has extensive expertise in CDI guidance and knowledge of documentation requirements relative to compliant coding and billing, in addition to EHR functionality to support documentation capture.

At the heart of AHIMA's mission and vision is documentation that supports quality health information. The CDIP certification confirms the commitment of AHIMA to globally improve and maintain quality information for those involved in healthcare as well as support the integrity of the patient's health record.

Eligibility

Candidates must meet *one* of the following eligibility requirements to sit for the CDIP examination:

- Hold an associate's degree or higher; or
- Hold a CCS®, CCS-P®, RHIT®, or RHIA® credential

While not required, the following are recommended:

- Minimum of two (2) years of clinical documentation integrity experience
- Associate's degree or higher in a healthcare or allied healthcare discipline
- Completion of coursework in the following topics:
  - Medical terminology
  - Human anatomy and physiology
  - Pathology
  - Pharmacology

Detailed information about the CDIP exam and academic eligibility requirements can be found at www.ahima.org/certification.

CDIP Exam Competency Statements

A certification examination is based on an explicit set of competencies. These competencies have been determined through a job analysis study conducted of practitioners. The competencies are subdivided into domains and tasks as listed here. The exam tests only content pertaining to these competencies. Each domain is allocated a predefined number of questions at specific cognitive levels to make up the examination.

Certified Documentation Improvement Practitioner (CDIP) Exam Content Outline

Domain 1 – Clinical Coding Practice

Tasks:

1. Use reference resources for code assignment
2. Identify the principal and secondary diagnoses in order to accurately reflect the patient's hospital course
3. Assign and sequence diagnosis and procedure codes
4. Apply coding conventions and guidelines related to diagnosis and procedure codes
5. Understand the assignment of the working and final DRG
6. Communicate with the coding/HIM staff to resolve discrepancies between the working and final DRGs, and to ensure coding and reimbursement updates are incorporated into practice

Domain 2 – Education and Leadership Development

Tasks:

1. Promote CDI efforts throughout the organization and health system, including administration
2. Create and nurture working relationships to support collaboration across multi-disciplinary teams
3. Develop documentation improvement projects
4. Collaborate with physician champions to promote CDI initiatives
5. Develop CDI policies and procedures in accordance with AHIMA practice briefs
6. Determine facility requirements for documentation of query responses in the record to establish official policy and procedures related to CDI query activities
7. Recognize a chain of command for resolving unanswered queries
8. Facilitate clinical documentation integrity by identifying educational topics and delivery methods for effective learning for an audience
9. Articulate the implications of accurate documentation and coding with respect to research, public health reporting, case management, and reimbursement

Domain 3 – Record Review and Document Clarification

Tasks:

1. Demonstrate comprehension of clinical documentation in health records
2. Identify and prioritize cases as part of the CDI review process
3. Identify gaps in documentation that may impact patient quality of care, code assignment, or reimbursement (e.g., command of disease process, clinical concepts, clinical validation opportunities, etc.)
4. Apply industry current best practices pertaining to query development and query processes
5. Identify strategies for obtaining query responses from providers and ensure provider query response is documented in the health record
6. Interact with providers to clarify documentation opportunities within the health record (e.g., patient quality indicators, Present on Admission (POA), acuteness/chronicity, complications, etc.)
7. Identify post-discharge query opportunities

Domain 4 – CDI Metrics and Statistics

Tasks:

1. Identify common dashboard metrics and monitor CDI departmental performance
2. Perform quality audits of CDI content to ensure compliance with institutional policies & procedures or national guidelines
3. Track metrics and interpret trends related to the physician query process (e.g., CDI perspective vs provider perspective)
4. Track and interpret data for physician benchmarking and trending
5. Compare institution with external institutional benchmarks
6. Identify common key performance metrics for CDI professionals
7. Use CDI data to adjust departmental workflow

Domain 5 – Compliance

Tasks:

1. Apply AHIMA and other industry standards in support of ethical CDI best practices
2. Monitor changes in the regulatory environment applicable to CDI activities to maintain compliance with all applicable agencies
3. Identify risks associated with technology (e.g., electronic health records, natural language processing (NLP), computer-assisted coding, etc.)
4. Identify situations when second level reviews are appropriate
5. Understand and appropriately use clinical validation queries
6. Identify and address non-compliant queries as part of a CDI workflow
7. Apply policies regarding various stages of the query process and time frames, including retention of queries, to avoid compliance risk

CDIP Exam Specifications

The CDIP is a timed exam. Candidates have three hours to complete the exam. The total number of questions on the exam is 140. There are 106 scored items and 34 pretest items. The exam is given in a computer-based format.

AHIMA exams contain a variety of questions or item types that require you to use your knowledge, skills, and/or experience to select the best answer. Each exam includes scored questions and pretest questions randomly distributed throughout the exam. Pretest questions are for data collection purpose and they do not count towards candidate's score.

The passing score for the CDIP is 300.

Competencies for CDIPs fall into domains. Each domain accounts for a specific percentage of the total questions on the certification exam. See the Exam Content Outline for greater detail.

How to Use This Book and Online Assessments

The CDIP practice exams in this book and on the accompanying online assessments test knowledge of content pertaining to the CDIP competencies published by AHIMA and available at ahima.org /certification. The multiple-choice practice questions and examinations in this book and the accompanying online assessments are presented in a similar format to those that might be found on the CDIP examination.

This book contains two multiple choice practice exams (with 140 questions each). Because each question is identified with one of the five CDIP domains, you will be able to determine whether you need knowledge or skill building in particular areas of the exam domains. Each question provides an answer rationale and reference with the correct answer. Pursuing the sources of these references will help you build your knowledge and skills in specific domains.

Retake the practice questions and examinations as many times as you like. Remember that to help build your knowledge and skills, you should review the references provided for all questions that you answered incorrectly.

The online assessments present the same two timed practice exams printed in the book and also includes a bonus practice exam for AHIMA-approved instructors. (Practice Exam 3 is a web-only bonus exam.) These exams can be run in practice mode—which allows you to work at your own pace—or exam mode—which simulates the three-hour timed exam experience. The practice questions and simulated practice exams can be set to be presented in random order, or you may choose to go through the questions in sequential order by domain. You may also choose to practice or test your skills on specific domains. For example, if you would like to build your skills in domain 2, you may choose only domain 2 questions for a given practice session.

INTRODUCTION

Clinical documentation integrity (CDI) strives to reflect the clinical needs of the patient, the acuity and chronicity of those conditions, and the actions performed by the provider to meet those needs. It has become integral to the success of an organization in quality performance, value-based care, fee-for-service, and population health initiatives. CDI professionals (CDIPs), sometimes called clinical documentation specialists (CDS), are key members of the quality revenue cycle and assist providers, ensuring their documentation correlates with the care they provide. This book is a learning tool to assist professionals in becoming certified in CDI and displaying their advanced skill set within the profession.

Exam Basics

Information pertaining to the Clinical Documentation Integrity Exam is posted on the American Health Information Management Association (AHIMA) website here. Please refer to the website to obtain the latest requirements and content information.

Test-Taking Tips

- **Learning Style**
  - We all learn differently and have different needs for optimal test-taking success.
  - Know what type of learner you are and utilize that to structure how you study.
    - Visual learners—like flashcards and lists to see the information for retention. This visualization allows seeing what you learned for recall.
    - Auditory—may need a study buddy for verbal reinforcement or repeat things aloud for retention.
    - Kinesthetic—struggle with sitting still learning; try studying in blocks and group studying. You like memory games, and playing along with others helps with retention for this type of learning.
- **Studying**
  - Identify your areas of weakness to target your focus.
  - Organize your references for studying. You can find references used for the text in the back of the book.
  - Utilize the practice exams to determine where learning deficits may exist and focus on reinforcement for those areas.
  - Pace yourself in studying. The CDIP Exam contains diverse content. Allow yourself adequate time for research and learning.
  - Make a schedule or plan for how or when you will study.
  - Write out query examples to practice query formulation.
- **Practice**
  - The CDIP Exam is time-based. Take and retake practice exams to assist you in getting prepared for time-based testing. Remember the time does not stop once begun, and you will answer questions until you have fully completed the exam or time has elapsed.
- **Content**
  - Know your coding principles and guidelines.
  - Know the query rules and how to query.
  - Understand and be familiar with pharmacology, clinical indicators, and disease process.
  - Read and review AHA Coding Clinic for *ICD-10-CM* and *ICD-10-PCS*.
  - Review American Medical Association *Current Procedural Terminology* (CPT) as related to the CDI function.
  - Recall and apply ethical standards in health information and coding.

CDI Hints for Success

- You should have a thorough knowledge of the disease process, clinical information, and treatments.
- Utilize national CDI and coding guidelines, not facility-specific guidelines.
- Review Coding Clinic and CPT Assistant; focus on most recent issues. Review newest to oldest issues and pay attention to topics that have been superseded/updated.
- Understand Medicare Severity Diagnosis Related Groups (MS-DRGs) and Ambulatory Payment Classifications (APCs) methodologies and MS-DRG structure and hierarchies.

- Know and identify how principal diagnoses, secondary diagnoses, and major comorbidities or complications (MCCs) and complications or comorbidities (CCs) impact MS-DRGs.
- Determine if you have a knowledge deficit in any common coding areas because your facility does not treat that type of patient. For example, some facilities do not provide services for newborns, deliveries, heart catheterizations, coronary artery bypass grafts (CABGs), or neonatal intensive care. If you work in such a facility, you will need to strategize how to gather expertise in these areas. One way to gain expertise is to review the coding exercises in a basic coding book and to use an encoder to determine the MS-DRGs associated with the exercises.
- Review the last two years of the *Journal of AHIMA* for informative topics including future nomenclatures, such as ICD-11, and the Health Insurance Portability and Accountability Act (HIPAA).
- Refer to ICD-10-CM/PCS MS-DRG Definitions Manual for assistance with MS-DRG structure.

CDI Metrics and Statistics

- Calculations will be included in the exam. The bases for some calculations are listed below.
  1. Case Mix Index (CMI). A measure of the relative complexity and severity of patients treated in a hospital. CMI serves as the basis for payment methodologies administered by the Centers for Medicare and Medicaid Services (CMS) as well as other third-party payers. A number of factors can affect a hospital's CMI, including volume changes in certain DRGs and documentation/coding improvements. CDI leadership should understand CMI fluctuations and declines in CMI. Through proper measurement and analysis, providers can identify ways to improve a stagnant or declining CMI. To understand a hospital's total CMI, the following five metrics are calculated as follows:
     - Overall CMI. Add the relative weights of all DRGs and divide by the total inpatient population, excluding psychiatric and rehabilitation patients.
     - Medical CMI. Add the relative weights of all medical DRGs and divide by the total medical inpatient population, excluding psychiatric and rehabilitation patients.
     - Surgical CMI. Add the relative weights of all surgical DRGs and divide by the total surgical inpatient population, excluding psychiatric and rehabilitation patients.
     - Adjusted CMI. Remove all high-weighted DRGs that are not typically influenced by coding and/ or clinical documentation improvements from the inpatient population, such as tracheotomies and transplants (MS-DRGs 1-17 and 652), excluding psychiatric and rehabilitation patients. Remove this volume from the overall population before repeating the calculation for total CMI outlined above. Some facilities may also eliminate low-weighted, high-volume DRGs (e.g., normal newborns).
     - Medical/surgical mix and volume-adjusted CMI. This calculation can help you determine the percentage by which CMI has changed over two equal quarterly periods (e.g., the first quarter of 2014 to the first quarter of 2015) and the resulting change in reimbursement for the designated time period.
       - Calculate medical/surgical mix and compare volumes from the two equal time periods.
       - Adjust the CMI to equalize these two components by freezing one period and adjusting the mix distribution and volume of the other period to match the frozen period.
       - Compare medical/surgical mix of the periods.
  2. Overall CMI, Medical CMI, and Surgical CMI. Separately determining the medical CMI and the surgical CMI will identify underlying problems masked in the overall CMI. Average medical CMI weights range from 1.0 to 1.15. A low-end overall medical CMI may indicate symptom DRGs and the need for a more specific principal diagnosis or missing complications and comorbidities (CCs) that should have been captured. Low medical CMIs may be heavily influenced by incorrectly documented and/or sequenced principal diagnoses.
  3. Adjusted CMI. Remove all tracheotomies and transplants (MS-DRGs 1-17 and 652), which are very high-weighted DRGs and have geometric mean length of stay (GMLOS) and average length of stay (ALOS) impact, without documentation improvement potential. This allows a focus on DRGs that will most likely be influenced by CDI efforts. Analysis of the adjusted CMI enables you to target underlying coding or documentation issues that need to be addressed.

4. Comparative Medical and Surgical Case Mix. Compare the volume of all inpatient cases in two comparable time periods, as well as the percentage of cases that are medical versus surgical, by calculating the medical/surgical mix and volume-adjusted CMI. Be sure to note losses and gains that may indicate the need for further investigation:

    *   Look at volume loss or medical/surgical mix change to determine if you are losing market share to competitors.
        *   Review the case types to see if they are moving to a different level of service (inpatient to ambulatory surgery or to observation).
        *   Review the CMI by service line to identify focus areas and break it down further by DRGs to see if CC capture rates or key DRG pairs are in the optimal DRG assignments.
5. Track and trend the following calculations:
    *   Percentage of one- to two-day length of stays in both periods. An increase in short-stay cases may be causing a decline in CMI. Consider benchmarking your length of stay against other hospitals to uncover any major differences. Understand the impact of CMS' Final Rule 1599, known as the "Two Midnight Rule," which affects patient level of care while in the hospital.
    *   CMI by each service line or by major diagnostic category. Perform this calculation for comparable time periods, such as six-month periods in different years, to determine if CMI has increased or decreased. This will help narrow down the root cause(s) of a declining overall CMI to a particular set of DRGs or service lines. Further investigation may indicate less-complex cases than anticipated or possible documentation/coding deficiencies or inaccuracies, such as lower CC capture rates.
    *   Overall CC capture rate, and then by individual DRG level. Compare the CC capture rate between two periods to determine focus areas. Providers with access to industry benchmarks for CC capture rates should use these as points of comparison in addition to their organizations' past performance. A CC capture rate may be measured against a previous year, but it still may be significantly behind industry performance if a provider compares it to others outside its facility.
    *   Present on Admission (POA). Track and trend POA indicator assignments of No (N). Conditions with a POA indicator of N indicate that the condition was not present on admission and occurred during the hospital stay. This may affect facility reimbursement and data reporting.
6. Compare the volume of distribution in key DRG pairs. For example, calculate the volume of complex versus simple pneumonia, chronic obstructive pulmonary disease (COPD) versus respiratory failure, and gastroenteritis versus dehydration. Review the distribution of cases in the higher-weighted DRGs compared to peers or industry benchmarks.
7. CDI coding DRG reconciliation. Review and monitor final coded DRG and assigned codes to concurrently assigned codes and DRGs. Identify CDI impacts and opportunities for CDI, coding, and physician education.

The Query Process

The CDIP must have a good understanding of the query process, whether retrospective or concurrent. Utilize the AHIMA guidance, "Guidelines for Achieving a Compliant Query Practice." Throughout, the exam questions and scenarios will test query knowledge in the form of identifying when to query, how to query, appropriateness of queries, and understanding of the principles of the query process.

The query is a communication tool used to clarify documentation in the health record for accurate code assignment. The desired outcome from a query is an update of a health record to better reflect a practitioner's intent and clinical thought processes, documented in a manner that supports accurate code assignment. The final coded diagnoses and procedures derived from the health record documentation should accurately reflect the patient's episode of care.

The generation of a query should be considered when the health record documentation

*   is conflicting, imprecise, incomplete, illegible, ambiguous, or inconsistent.
*   describes or is associated with clinical indicators without a definitive relationship to an underlying diagnosis.
*   includes clinical indicators, diagnostic evaluation, and/or treatment not related to a specific condition or procedure.
*   provides a diagnosis without underlying clinical validation.
*   is unclear for the present on admission indicator assignment.

Although open-ended queries are preferred, multiple-choice and yes/no queries are also acceptable under certain circumstances (AHIMA 2013b).

Problematic Diagnoses

For the CDI, there are a number of diagnoses that require increased education, monitoring, and collaboration with providers. Utilize and complete the table below to increase your critical thinking, understanding of these conditions, and how they impact CDI. Make your own table as needed to help you focus on your needs.

Diagnosis	Definition	Medications/Treatment	Tests	CDI Focus
Blood loss anemia	Reduction of red blood cells	Transfusion iron replacement therapy	CBC (hemoglobin/hematocrit) coagulation testing (PT/PTT)	• Acute chronic • Source/cause of blood loss
Congestive heart failure				
Coma in conditions; e.g., hepatitis				
Encephalopathy				
Malnutrition				
Neoplasms (primary vs. secondary)				
Pneumonia				
Renal failure				
Respiratory failure				
Sepsis				
Shock (septic, related to trauma/procedure)				

Diagnostic Tests and Interpretation

Ensuring there is sufficient clinical knowledge is important for any CDI. Common lab tests as related to signs, symptoms, treatment, and documentation within the health record will be addressed within the exam.

- Complete blood count
- Red blood cells
- White blood cells
- Platelets
- Hemoglobin
- Hematocrit
- Mean corpuscular volume
- Blood chemistry tests/basic metabolic panel
- Blood glucose
- Calcium
- Electrolytes
- BUN/creatinine
- Blood enzyme tests
- D-dimer
- Serum lactate
- Troponin
- Creatine kinase
- Lipoprotein

- Total cholesterol
- LDL ("bad") cholesterol
- HDL ("good") cholesterol
- Triglycerides
- Blood clotting tests

You have taken an important step as a future CDIP. Much success to you all.

PRACTICE EXAM 1

Domain 1 *Clinical Coding Practice*

1. A 54-year-old female has been seen in outpatient surgery for a laparoscopic appendectomy. The patient has hypertension, diabetes mellitus Type II, on insulin, appendicitis, and had a cholecystitis with cholecystectomy in 2015; removed. All diagnoses except _____ would be coded:

   a. Hypertension

   b. Diabetes mellitus Type II

   c. Cholecystitis

   d. Appendicitis

2. A 63-year-old male presents to outpatient surgery for prostatectomy with benign prostatic hypertrophy. After arriving in the OR and prior to induction of anesthesia, the patient began to experience substernal chest pain. The patient takes Lasix for a long-standing history of congestive heart failure. The prostate surgery is canceled, and the patient was observed for 10 hours and discharged. The patient's first-listed diagnosis should be

   a. Benign prostatic hypertrophy

   b. Congestive heart failure

   c. Canceled surgery

   d. Chest pain

3. A 50-year-old patient has a diagnosis of hypertension, on Amlodipine and Humalog for Type II diabetes and was seen on follow-up. The provider adjusted the dosage of Amlodipine and performed an A1C for glucose control. An audit was performed, and the auditor stated these diagnoses should not be coded.

   a. This is correct; only acute conditions should be coded.

   b. This is incorrect; chronic conditions can be reported if treated.

   c. The physician must document the reason for this visit.

   d. Only the hypertension can be coded, as it was adjusted.

4. A patient is admitted for pneumonia and acute renal failure. The patient is placed on IV antibiotics with diuresis on admission. The principal diagnosis would be

   a. Pneumonia because the patient was given IV drug therapy

   b. Acute renal failure because this condition is stated as acute

   c. The pneumonia or the acute renal failure could be the principal diagnosis

   d. Neither, because the physician did not state which one was principal

5. When physician documentation states SpO2 room air < 91%, ABG shows pO2 on room air less than 60 mm, and proceeds with intubation and/or initiations of BiPAP, the diagnosis is most likely

   a. Respiratory failure

   b. Acute respiratory failure

   c. Chronic respiratory failure

   d. Acute or chronic respiratory failure

6. Documentation review shows testing of cardiac troponin, echocardiography with a plan for percutaneous coronary intervention (PCI). The patient is most likely to be evaluated for

    a. Acute myocardial infarction

    b. Chest pain

    c. Gastroesophageal reflux disease (GERD)

    d. Cerebrovascular accident (CVA)

7. During chart review, it is documented that the patient has sepsis. The CDI professional should review the labs for testing to identify increased levels of a substance made by muscle tissue and by red blood cells, which carry oxygen from the lungs to other parts of the body and can lead to a type of acidosis. This test is called a

    a. Complete blood count (CBC)

    b. Chem 8

    c. Kidney function test

    d. Lactic acid

8. On CDI review, it was noted that the patient stumbled on the sidewalk, and workup reveals a small pelvic fracture at the symphysis. The MD states she received Reclast annually. The CDI professional should query for what diagnosis to reflect complexity and severity?

    a. Fracture

    b. Osteoporotic fracture

    c. Cause of fracture

    d. Traumatic fracture

9. On CDI review, it was noted that the patient stumbled on the sidewalk, and workup reveals a small pelvic fracture at the symphysis. The MD states she received Reclast annually. Which code category should be used for code assignment?

    a. M80

    b. M81

    c. M82

    d. M83

10. When a patient is admitted with respiratory failure and another acute condition (e.g., myocardial infarction, cerebrovascular, aspiration pneumonia), the principal diagnosis will ____.

    a. be the same in every situation

    b. be respiratory failure

    c. not be the same in every situation

    d. be the acute condition

11. The AMA publishes the *Current Procedural Terminology* (CPT). CPT is updated how often?

    a. Monthly

    b. Quarterly

    c. Annually

    d. Anytime code updates are needed

12. What terminology is currently being used in electronic health record (EHR) systems as a clinical reference terminology to capture data for problem lists and patient assessments at the point of care?

    a. CPT

    b. ICD-CM

    c. ICD-PCS

    d. SNOMED CT

13. This coding convention must be used in conjunction with an underlying condition code; they must be listed following the underlying condition:

    a. Code also

    b. Multiple coding

    c. Code pair

    d. Etiology/manifestation

14. If _____ appears in a code title in the alphabetic index (either under a main term or subterm) or an instructional note in the Tabular List, the classification presumes a causal relationship between the two conditions linked by these terms in the Alphabetic Index or Tabular List.

    a. By

    b. Code also

    c. With

    d. Relevant to

15. The physician documents congestive heart failure, hypertension, and chronic obstructive pulmonary disease in the diagnostic statement on the discharge summary. The coding team will

    a. Assign the diagnoses

    b. Refer to CDI for clinical review

    c. Review for clinical support

    d. Not assign the codes for the diagnoses

16. A patient was admitted with fever, chills, headache, and cough. The physician suspects the patient has COVID but the repeated tests are negative. The physician documents COVID as final diagnosis. This final diagnosis assigned should be

    a. Exposure to COVID

    b. Signs and symptoms

    c. COVID

    d. Negative COVID test

17. This patient has old-age dementia. She also has Parkinson's disease and has trouble drinking her morning tea due to tremors. Coding conventions consider these conditions as

    a. Due to dementia

    b. Etiology and manifestation conventions

    c. Not related

    d. Inclusion term conventions

18. Patient was admitted with diastolic dysfunction, hypertension, acute pyelonephritis, and chronic obstructive pulmonary disease. Which medication below would be given to treat her hypertension?

    a. Methotrexate

    b. Singular

    c. Amlodipine

    d. Coreg

19. In the evening, Mrs. Darling was admitted with fatigue, tachypnea, rigors/shivers, temp of 102, hypotension at 110/78. An ulcer is noted on her right heel with purulent drainage. The hospitalist prescribed Cefepime. This drug is being prescribed for what possible condition?

    a. Pneumonia

    b. Sepsis

    c. Febrile illness

    d. Septic shock

20. Sallie has been wheezing throughout the night. Her mother presents to the ED stating she needs a bronchodilator. She has often experienced being given only steroids to treat her recurrent asthma exacerbations. Which of the below are bronchodilator(s)?

    a. Zyrtec

    b. Prednisone

    c. Spiriva

    d. Flonase

21. Coronary artery disease and diabetes can increase your risk of congestive heart failure (CHF). Signs and symptoms of CHF include which of the following:

    a. Night sweats

    b. Polydipsia

    c. Cardiac arrest

    d. Edema

22. Mrs. Day was admitted with complaints of severe back and abdominal pain with nausea and vomiting. She was seen in the ED multiple times over the past 6 months, and records show a weight loss of 20 pounds. She states she has had difficulty eating and smoking and has been unable to see her primary care physician. Abdominal CT shows liver enlargement; MRI ordered. Patient does appear to be jaundiced, with thinning skin and significant muscle/fat loss. It is determined the patient has severe weight loss, inability to eat, and vomiting. This patient should be given

    a. Glucose

    b. Calcium

    c. TPN

    d. None of the above

23. Janet was diagnosed with Type I diabetes at age 6. She has been taking long-acting insulin since the day she was diagnosed. She is being treated with

    a. Novolog

    b. Lantus

    c. Humulin

    d. Humalog

24. Mr. Baker has been suffering from Alzheimer's and has had problems remembering to take his medications. He has a history of diabetes with peripheral neuropathy and rheumatoid arthritis. His caregiver gives him_____ for Alzheimer's.

    a. Aricept

    b. Namenda

    c. Abilify

    d. Both A and B

25. Mrs. Day was admitted with complaints of severe back and abdominal pain with nausea and vomiting. She was seen in the ED multiple times over the past 6 months, and records show a weight loss of 20 pounds. She states she has had difficulty eating and smoking and has been unable to see her primary care physician. Abdominal CT shows liver enlargement; MRI ordered. Patient does appear to be jaundiced, with thinning skin and significant muscle/fat loss. It is determined the patient has severe weight loss, inability to eat, and vomiting. This physician should be queried for

    a. Sepsis

    b. Cirrhosis

    c. Malnutrition

    d. Morbid obesity

26. The drugs Lotensin, Vasotec, and Accupril are all

    a. ACE inhibitors

    b. Vasopressors

    c. Diuretics

    d. None of the above

27. Ambien is often used to treat

    a. Appetite disorders

    b. Attention deficit disorder

    c. Insomnia

    d. Irritable bowel syndrome

28. This blood test measures how liver and kidneys are performing and can be found in the liver function test and comprehensive metabolic panel (CMP).

    a. Amylase

    b. Albumin

    c. Neutrophils

    d. Lipase

29. Sep-3 includes which lab value to measure low oxygen levels caused by severe infection and/or shock?

    a. Kinase

    b. Ammonia

    c. Lactic acid

    d. Oxygen

30. A 70-year-old male was seen in the clinic with blood in the urine with frequent urination, incontinence, and pain with fatigue 3 weeks ago. With a PSA of 13 and enlarged prostate on digital exam, a biopsy was performed with a diagnosis of prostate cancer, Stage I. Due to patient's age and no desire for further treatment, it was decided the patient should undergo

    a. Cryosurgery

    b. Transurethral resection of the prostate (TURP)

    c. Watchful waiting

    d. Chemotherapy

31. Who is responsible for the content, quality, and authentication of the discharge summary?

    a. Attending physician

    b. Head nurse

    c. Consulting physician

    d. Admitting nurse

32. The clinical statement "microscopic sections of the gallbladder reveal a surface lined by tall columnar cells of uniform size and shape" would be documented on which health record form?

    a. Operative report

    b. Pathology report

    c. Discharge summary

    d. Nursing note

33. A patient was admitted to the ICU with acute respiratory failure. The patient has a history of emphysema. The patient was placed on mechanical ventilation. Lab results on day 4 following vent showed WBCs of 13,000 and sputum culture showed pseudomonas with new infiltrate on chest x-ray. The CDI should be looking for documentation of what diagnosis to support this scenario?

    a. Bacterial asthma

    b. Pneumonia with emphysema

    c. Sepsis

    d. Ventilator-associated pneumonia

34. A condition characterized by shortness of breath, weight gain, pedal edema, fatigue, difficulty breathing when lying down, and commonly treated with Lasix is

    a. Cardiomyopathy

    b. Congestive heart failure

    c. Asthma

    d. Coronary artery disease

35. A type of seizure that can cause a person to cry out, lose consciousness, fall to the ground, and have muscle jerks or spasms is called tonic-clonic, or

    a. Petit mal

    b. Absence

    c. Grand mal

    d. Focal

36. This condition is a common side effect of chemotherapy and can increase the risk of infection.

    a. Anemia

    b. Plasma rejection

    c. Leukocytosis

    d. Neutropenia

37. The ankle brachial index is commonly used to diagnose

    a. Peripheral arterial disease (PAD)

    b. High cholesterol

    c. Vascular disease

    d. Malleolar disease

38. Mr. Jones has had rheumatoid arthritis for a number of years. He is most likely taking which medication below?

    a. Ritalin

    b. Neulasta

    c. Remicade

    d. Epogen

39. A patient was prescribed Lovenox. Lovenox is usually prescribed as a

    a. Antibiotic

    b. Anticoagulant

    c. Antiemetic

    d. Chemotherapeutic

40. This drug is an anti-epileptic and also used to treat diabetic neuropathy.

    a. Amlodipine

    b. Phenobarbital

    c. Angiotensin

    d. Lyrica

41. This report document is a reflection of the hospital visit and is sometimes required for final coding.

    a. History and Physical

    b. Consultation

    c. Progress Note

    d. Discharge Summary

42. The cooperating parties include all of the following except:

    a. American Health Information Management Association (AHIMA)

    b. American Hospital Association (AHA)

    c. National Center for Health Statistics (NCHS)

    d. Centers for Medicare and Medicaid Services (CMS)

43. MS-DRGs are categorized by:

    a. Major Diagnostic Category (MDC)

    b. Ambulatory Payment Category (APC)

    c. Complications and Comorbidities (CCs)

    d. All Patient Refined Groups (APR)

44. The CDI supervisor is reviewing how often diagnoses that are MCCs or CCs are coded. This is called a

    a. Coding Rate

    b. Capture Rate

    c. Severity Index

    d. Case Mix Index

45. You are the coding supervisor, and you are doing an audit of outpatient coding. Robert Thompson was seen in the outpatient department with a chronic cough, and the record states "rule out lung cancer." What should have been coded as the patient's diagnosis?

    a. Chronic cough

    b. Observation and evaluation without need for further medical care

    c. Diagnosis of unknown etiology

    d. Lung cancer

Domain 2   *Education and Leadership Development*

46. A CDI program should have a governance or oversight committee composed of manager of CDI, physician CDI leader, and

    a. ED physician

    b. Medical staff chair

    c. Executive management

    d. CDI staff

47. What is the study of morality using the principles, theories, and decision-making frameworks of philosophy?

    a. Ethics

    b. Compliance

    c. Regulatory compliance

    d. Code of conduct

48. The physician leader for CDI should have experience and expertise consistent with

   a. Inpatient

   b. Outpatient

   c. Responsibilities demanded by the CDI program

   d. Compliance

49. It is ideal that the CDI program leader should report to

   a. The CMO

   b. The CEO

   c. The CDI director

   d. Compliance

50. ABC hospital is starting a new CDI program. It is essential that the oversight committee gain support of the

   a. ICU staff

   b. ED staff

   c. Coding staff

   d. Medical staff

51. When implementing a new CDI program, the CDI operations team should meet at least

   a. Daily

   b. Weekly

   c. Monthly

   d. Quarterly

52. HIM and coding departments, case management and utilization review, medical staff and provider leadership, and executive leadership are examples of

   a. CDI stakeholders

   b. CDI team

   c. CDI task force

   d. None of the above

53. CDI programs must have clearly defined goals. Examples of goals include obtain clinical documentation that captures the patient SOI and ROM; identify and clarify missing, conflicting, or nonspecific provider documentation related to diagnoses and procedures; support accurate diagnostic and procedural coding; MS-DRG assignment, leading to appropriate reimbursement, and

   a. Complete coding more quickly

   b. Improve documentation to reflect quality and outcome scores

   c. Increase denials

   d. Improve case management

54. To demonstrate that the goals and benefits of a CDI program are being achieved, track and trend

    a. CDI staff

    b. Coded accounts

    c. Key performance indicators (KPIs)

    d. DRGs

55. Some organizations make provider queries:

    a. A permanent component of the medical record

    b. Part of the discharge summary

    c. Part of the case management notes

    d. Unavailable

56. A physician that has clinical and leadership experience that champions the CDI program is called a

    a. Chair

    b. Director

    c. Physician advisor

    d. Supervisor

57. When starting a new CDI program, a _____ audit of previously billed records should be performed to determine the volumes and types of potential query opportunities that exist.

    a. Chart

    b. Retrospective

    c. Billing

    d. Concurrent

58. Dr. Tom has been sent multiple queries, and the CDI professionals have not been getting a response from him. The CDI manager should

    a. Not be concerned

    b. Call the physician

    c. Follow up with leadership

    d. Follow the policy for unanswered queries

59. When a query remains unanswered, it can be designated as incomplete and assigned as delinquent, sent through the medical peer review process, or

    a. Disregarded

    b. Sent to physician advisor for direct physician follow-up

    c. Assigned to any provider

    d. Send to CMO to complete

60. Cindy is a new CDI. She will be in department-specific training from 90 days up to 1 year. This training is called

    a. Education

    b. Assessment

    c. Orientation

    d. Professional development

61. It is recommended that the CDI supervisor/manager meet with new staff and inform them of their progress, check off items that are completed or closed, and

    a. Plan CDI week

    b. Complete their day

    c. Review charts

    d. Identify learning needs

62. CDI programs should have written policies and procedures to support operational efficiency and

    a. To record everything

    b. To help meet goals

    c. To reduce compliance risk

    d. To improve respect for the program

63. The CDI query paper trail helps to support the organization in the investigation or audit process. The paper trail shows why the query was asked, how the physician responded, and

    a. The length of the query

    b. How the query was asked

    c. The time of the query

    d. Who saw the query

64. CDI has recently found out there are key departments they should meet with regularly and share information. Important feedback loops for CDI are HIM, compliance, and

    a. Privacy

    b. Security

    c. Denials management

    d. Human resources

65. The discharge summary lists a diagnosis that is different than the diagnosis listed on the pathology report. The CDI should

    a. Follow the diagnosis on the discharge summary

    b. Use the diagnosis for the tissue collected on the path

    c. Compare to the H&P for consistency

    d. Query the attending physician for the final diagnosis

66. CDI staff should begin concurrent review on what day of a patient's admission?

    a. Day one

    b. Day two

    c. Day of discharge

    d. Day prior to discharge

67. Dr. Hayes is new to CDI and would like more training in CDI. The organization may

    a. Bring in an external physician to function as CMO

    b. Bring in an external physician to teach the physician and assist with responsibilities

    c. Partner the physician with compliance

    d. Partner the physician with an ED physician

68. What is a written statement that sets forth the purpose and philosophy of an organization or group?

    a. Mission statement

    b. Policy statement

    c. Philosophy

    d. Vision

69. In a CDI program, who is responsible for facilitating development of the mission?

    a. CDI manager

    b. CDI physician advisor

    c. CEO of organization

    d. Chair of the CDI steering committee

70. Which area below should not be a benefit of an outpatient CDI program?

    a. Improved quality of clinical documentation

    b. Improved charge capture

    c. Improved care coordination

    d. Reduced payment errors

71. An outpatient CDI professional should have in-depth knowledge of the *International Classification of Diseases, 10th Revision, Clinical Modification* (ICD-10-CM), *Current Procedural Terminology/ Healthcare Common Procedure Coding System* (CPT/HCPCS) coding, and

    a. Outpatient prospective payment system (OPPS) guidelines

    b. Outpatient scheduling

    c. Diagnosis-related groups (DRGs)

    d. Case mix index

72. When working with an external vendor, an organization should negotiate the statement of work (SOW) for the project and

    a. Staff

    b. Time

    c. Work

    d. Costs

73. The coding supervisor is concerned that patients diagnosed with carcinoid colon tumors were miscoded as malignant during the last 6 months. To address this situation, what work processes could be undertaken?

    a. Obtain the cases of carcinoid colon tumors from the cancer registry, obtain the cases of malignant colon tumors from the billing system, import both lists into a spreadsheet, and compare them. The cases in the cancer registry but not coded as carcinoid in the billing system are likely malignant and should be manually reviewed.

    b. Compare the cases from the chart completion software with the billing software. Identify the cases that are not in the billing system. These cases should be manually reviewed to ensure they are not carcinoid tumors.

    c. Obtain the cases of malignant colon tumors from both the cancer registry and the billing system; import both lists into a spreadsheet and compare them. Identify the cases that are not in the tumor registry but are coded as malignant in the billing system. These cases should be manually reviewed to ensure they are not carcinoid tumors.

    d. Compare the cases from the transcription tracking software with the billing system. Identify the cases that are not in the transcription tracking software and are in the billing system. These cases should be manually reviewed to ensure they are not carcinoid tumors.

74. Under which of the following circumstances does a healthcare entity lose a potential increase in reimbursement when a hospital-acquired condition (HAC) is coded without a POA indicator of "Y"?

    a. When the HAC is the only Complication or Comorbidity (CC)/Major Complication or Comorbidity (MCC) on the account

    b. When the HAC is listed as the principal diagnosis

    c. When the HAC is coded along with a surgical procedure

    d. When the HAC is the only diagnosis listed

75. AHIMA's "Standards of Ethical Coding" apply to which of the following setting(s)?

    a. Acute inpatient

    b. Outpatient

    c. Provider offices

    d. All settings

76. The Uniform Hospital Discharge Data Set (UHDDS) definition of principal procedure indicates that the principal procedure can be assigned for which of the following?

    a. Addressing complications

    b. Exploration

    c. Diagnostic

    d. Clinical evaluation

77. It is unethical for a coding professional to query

    a. Retrospectively

    b. When the response will impact reimbursement

    c. Based on information in a previous encounter

    d. Multiple times on the same patient record

78. In addition to credentialed coding professionals, AHIMA's "Standards of Ethical Coding" apply to which of the following groups?

    a. Non-credentialed coding professionals and students

    b. Students and attorneys

    c. Attorneys and auditors

    d. Case managers and non-credentialed coding professionals

79. Which patient-specific UHDDS items also have the potential to have an impact on MS-DRG assignment?

    a. Race and residence

    b. Residence and sex

    c. Sex and discharge disposition

    d. Discharge disposition and race

80. After consulting with a physician, a coding supervisor has issued an internal policy stating that all bedside debridement be coded as excisional. Is this an ethical practice for a coding professional to follow? Why or why not?

    a. Yes, physician guidance provided basis for the policy

    b. Yes, coding professionals must follow internal policies of the facilities where they are employed

    c. No, coding supervisors cannot make internal policies without approval of the administration

    d. No, internal policies cannot conflict with requirements provided in coding guidelines, conventions, and so on

81. What is the term used when protected health information has been disclosed inappropriately?

    a. Exposure

    b. Breach

    c. Violation

    d. Infraction

82. The APR-DRG system does not include

    a. MCCs

    b. CCs

    c. HCCs

    d. MCCs or CCs

83. This site is utilized to review physician and hospital profiles.

    a. Healthgrades

    b. CMS

    c. MAC

    d. PEPPER

84. According to the UHDDS, Section III, the definition of other diagnoses is all conditions that

    a. Coexist at the time of admission, that develop subsequently, or that affect the treatment received or the length of stay

    b. Receive evaluation and are documented by the physician

    c. Receive clinical evaluation, therapeutic treatment, further evaluation, extend the length of stay, increase nursing monitoring/care

    d. Are considered to be essential by the physicians involved and are reflected in the record

Domain 3   *Record Review and Document Clarification*

Select the appropriate MS-DRG for the following scenario using the table below:

MS-DRG	MDC	MS-DRG Title	Weights
186	MED	PLEURAL EFFUSION WITH MCC	1.5438
187	MED	PLEURAL EFFUSION WITH CC	1.0329
188	MED	PLEURAL EFFUSION WITHOUT CC/MCC	0.7295
189	MED	PULMONARY EDEMA AND RESPIRATORY FAILURE	1.2261
190	MED	CHRONIC OBSTRUCTIVE PULMONARY DISEASE WITH MCC	1.1251
191	MED	CHRONIC OBSTRUCTIVE PULMONARY DISEASE WITH CC	0.8843
192	MED	CHRONIC OBSTRUCTIVE PULMONARY DISEASE WITHOUT CC/MCC	0.6956
193	MED	SIMPLE PNEUMONIA AND PLEURISY WITH MCC	1.3120
194	MED	SIMPLE PNEUMONIA AND PLEURISY WITH CC	0.8639
195	MED	SIMPLE PNEUMONIA AND PLEURISY WITHOUT CC/MCC	0.6658
199	MED	PNEUMOTHORAX WITH MCC	1.7900
200	MED	PNEUMOTHORAX WITH CC	1.0765
201	MED	PNEUMOTHORAX WITHOUT CC/MCC	0.7096
202	MED	BRONCHITIS AND ASTHMA WITH CC/MCC	0.9670
203	MED	BRONCHITIS AND ASTHMA WITHOUT CC/MCC	0.7070

85. A 43-year-old patient presents with shortness of breath, elevated white blood cell count, and fever. Repeat chest x-rays show minimal consolidation. The physician documents a final diagnosis of pneumonia. Past medical history is significant for diabetes on Novolog and some neuropathy. The final DRG is

    a. 193

    b. 194

    c. 195

    d. 202

86. Susan is performing her daily CDI initial reviews. The patient was admitted with difficulty breathing and 3+ pedal edema. The physician states: no evidence of heart failure on the admission progress notes, continue home meds, and low-salt diet. The discharge summary states: congestive heart failure present on admission. This conflicting documentation should be clarified by the

    a. Consulting physician

    b. Attending physician

    c. Emergency physician

    d. Physician extender

87. CMS defines conditions like fat embolism and Stage III and IV pressure ulcers that are not present on admission to the hospital as

    a. Invalid for code assignment

    b. Hospital-acquired conditions

    c. Centennial conditions

    d. Hospital incidents

88. Per the CMS "Conditions of Participation," this document should be completed no more than 30 days before or 24 hours after admission.

    a. Emergency room report

    b. Consultation report

    c. History and physical report

    d. Discharge summary

89. Gina is a new CDI professional. She is validating whether Piperacillin was given to a patient. She should review the

    a. History and physical

    b. Physician notes

    c. Operative report

    d. Medication administration records (MARs)

90. Medicare Advantage provides expanded coverage of many healthcare services for Medicare beneficiaries outside of fee-for-service (FFS). This is a Medicare Part

    a. A

    b. B

    c. C

    d. D

91. What is a secondary condition that arises during hospitalization and is thought to increase the length of stay (LOS) called?

    a. Complication and comorbidity

    b. Intensity of service and severity of illness

    c. Complex complication

    d. Risk-adjusted

92. A patient presented with nausea, vomiting, and diarrhea for 3 days. The patient had a blood pressure of 80/42, creatine level 2.1, with a baseline creatin of 1.0 and lactic 3.6. The patient's GI panel and stool culture were negative. The patient was treated with empiric antibiotics and aggressive IV fluid resuscitation. Discharge summary diagnoses were gastroenteritis and AKI. What other condition could be considered based on the documentation?

    a. Hypovolemic shock

    b. Sepsis

    c. Acute renal failure

    d. No condition to query

93. This is a 75-year-old male with advanced dementia and rheumatoid arthritis, COPD on 2L nasal cannula at home. He presented with fever, productive cough of green sputum, and leukocytosis and was diagnosed with pneumonia. The patient had right middle lobe infiltrate on CXR. Speech Therapy placed the patient on a modified diet for dysphasia. The patient was treated with IV cefepime and Zosyn for 5 days and discharged on oral Augmentin for an additional 7 days. What would you query for?

    a. Pneumonia

    b. Gram-negative or aspiration pneumonia

    c. Sepsis

    d. No condition to query

94. Patient presented with shortness of breath, orthopnea, and bilateral extremity edema. ProBNP at 2752, CXR cardio eagle with interstitial edema. Crackles were heard in the lungs. Echocardiogram showed EF 57% and severe aortic stenosis. The patient was treated with IV Lasix. Discharge diagnosis was fluid overload with severe aortic stenosis. What other condition could be considered?

    a. Pleural effusion

    b. Cardiomyopathy

    c. Acute diastolic congestive heart failure (CHF)

    d. No condition to query

95. This patient presents with sudden numbness and weakness of the right arm. Patient's son states he appeared confused, with trouble speaking and with some problems walking. MRI performed and tPA is ordered. What condition could the physician be treating and would require query?

    a. Transient ischemic attack (TIA)

    b. Malignant neoplasm of the brain

    c. Bell's palsy

    d. Ischemic stroke

96. This 55-year-old patient is here following a visit last month for alcohol intoxication with long-standing abuse. The patient has a history of hepatitis and chronic renal failure. Patient is noted to have thrombocytopenia and elevated albumin, BUN, and SGOT and SGPT. Biliary atresia is noted on MRI. Based on information in this scenario, what condition could the physician be treating and would require query?

    a. Acute cholecystitis

    b. Thrombocytopenia

    c. Alcoholic cirrhosis

    d. Acute biliary disease

97. This 58-year-old male presented to the hospital with acute chest pain. A 12-lead EKG showed ST elevation. What type of MI is this commonly referred to?

    a. Type II MI

    b. STEMI

    c. NSTEMI

    d. 12 lead MI

98. Patient's final diagnosis on the discharge summary states abdominal pain, unclear etiology. The progress notes and the GI consult state recurrent colitis. This documentation

    a. Requires no query

    b. Should be coded as stated on the discharge summary

    c. Should be coded as stated in the progress notes

    d. Should be queried for clarification due to conflicting documentation

99. Mrs. Smith has had multiple admissions for chronic pancreatitis. She has had malaise and cachexia. Her weight 3 months ago was 135 and weight this admission is 120. She has been unable to keep her meals down due to diarrhea, nausea, and vomiting. The patient is quite frail and requires meal replacement. The patient will begin protein shakes six times per day, and home health has been ordered to assist with nutrition and other duties. The CDI professional should consider what diagnosis in formulating the query?

    a. Acute pancreatitis

    b. Pancreatic cancer

    c. Malnutrition

    d. All of the above

100. Queries may be either verbal or written and may be generated

    a. Concurrently

    b. Prebill

    c. Retrospectively

    d. All of the above

101. Queries should be performed by

    a. Any clinician informed in the patient care

    b. Nursing CDI professionals only

    c. Coding CDI professionals only

    d. Professionals trained and educated in the compliant query process

102. Query: The patient had a hysterectomy with removal of ovaries. This discharge summary states uterine mass. A diagnosis of uterine cancer is stated on the pathology report. Please document uterine cancer on the discharge summary. This query is

    a. Leading

    b. Nonleading

    c. Appropriate

    d. Not required

103. This 72-year-old patient has swelling in her lower extremities and tiredness with weakness. The patient has a history of congestive heart failure and was asked to elevate when lying down. She has shortness of breath and echocardiogram shows ventricular dysfunction and ejection fraction has been decreased at less than 28%. Her BNP is at 1089 on this admission. The CDI professional should consider what diagnosis in formulating the query?

    a. Combined diastolic and systolic heart failure

    b. Congestive systolic heart failure

    c. Acute and chronic systolic heart failure

    d. Acute and chronic diastolic heart failure

104. Mr. Ames presented through the ED with extreme fatigue, shortness of breath, abdominal pain, and melanic stools. He stated he noticed this last week but was hesitant to see the doctor. EGD and colonoscopy were performed, which showed duodenal ulcer with some evidence of bleed. The CDI professional should consider what diagnosis in formulating the query?

    a. Anemia

    b. Acute blood loss anemia

    c. Source of bleed

    d. Nothing additional

105. This patient was admitted following a sports accident that resulted in a traumatic brain injury (TBI). On discharge, it is noted the patient continues to have no feeling or mobility in the lower extremities on neuro checks. MRI shows injury of the lumbar spine and spinal contusion. The CDI professional should consider what diagnosis in formulating the query?

    a. Paraplegia

    b. Quadriplegia

    c. Monoplegia

    d. Biplegia

106. The patient presented with breathing difficulty, cough, mucus production, and wheezing. The patient was placed on nasal canula, given albuterol, atrovent with corticosteroids. The CDI professional should consider what diagnosis in formulating the query?

    a. COPD

    b. COPD with exacerbation

    c. Bronchitis

    d. Pneumonia

107. A patient was admitted to the hospital with unstable angina and congestive heart failure. The unstable angina is treated with nitrates, and intravenous Lasix is given to manage the heart failure. What is the appropriate coding action?

    a. Assign only the code for the congestive heart failure.

    b. Assign the codes for the unstable angina and congestive heart failure, sequence either first.

    c. Query the physician about which diagnoses to code.

    d. Assign only the code for the unstable angina.

108. The most challenging type of provider query is issued for

    a. Determining cause and effect

    b. Establishing clinical validation

    c. Resolving documentation conflict

    d. Clarifying acuity or specificity

109. A patient is admitted with a high temperature, lethargy, hypotension, tachycardia, oliguria, and elevated WBC. The patient also has more than 100,000 organisms of *Escherichia coli* per cc of urine. The attending physician documents "urosepsis." What is the next step for the coding professional?

    a. Code sepsis as the principal with a secondary diagnosis of urinary tract infection due to *E. coli*.

    b. Code urinary tract infection with sepsis as a secondary diagnosis.

    c. Query the physician to determine if the patient is being treated for sepsis, highlighting the clinical signs and symptoms.

    d. Ask the physician whether the patient had septic shock so that this may be used as the principal diagnosis.

110. A patient has findings suggestive of chronic obstructive pulmonary disease (COPD) on chest x-ray. The attending physician mentions the x-ray finding in one progress note but no medication, treatment, or further evaluation is provided. The coding professional should

    a. Query the attending physician regarding the x-ray finding

    b. Code the condition because the documentation reflects it

    c. Question the radiologist regarding whether to code this condition

    d. Use a code from abnormal findings to reflect the condition

111. A 64-year-old female is admitted to the hospital with nausea, vomiting, and edema. The patient has a history of diabetes and takes Metformin and Lisinopril as prescribed. Blood sugar and blood pressure are monitored while admitted. On the discharge summary, the final diagnoses of acute renal failure and diabetes are documented. What is the query opportunity for this record?

    a. Is the acute renal failure linked to the diabetes?

    b. Does the patient have hypertension?

    c. Does the patient have chronic renal failure?

    d. Is the diabetes out of control?

112. A 56-year-old woman is admitted to an acute-care facility from a skilled nursing facility. The patient has multiple sclerosis and hypertension. During hospitalization, a decubitus ulcer is found and debrided at the bedside by a physician. There is no typed operative report and no pathology report. The coding professional should

    a. Use an excisional debridement code, as these charts are rarely reviewed to verify the excisional debridement

    b. Code with a non-excisional debridement procedure code

    c. Query the healthcare provider who performed the procedure to determine if the debridement was excisional

    d. Eliminate the procedure code altogether

113. Patient presents with lower left quadrant abdominal pain with normal white cell count. X-ray showed sigmoid diverticulitis. Patient underwent a resection of sigmoid colon with anastomosis, developing a postoperative ileus after surgery. Nausea abated after resolution of the ileus. What is the query opportunity for this case?

    a. Was the diverticulitis perforated?

    b. Was the nausea postoperative?

    c. Was there an associated abscess with the diverticulitis?

    d. Was the postoperative ileus a complication?

114. Compliant multiple-choice queries:

    a. Must contain every possible option for the provider to choose from

    b. Can provide a new diagnosis with supporting clinical indicators

    c. Should provide a minimum of three options

    d. Are the preferred query format for establishing present on admission (POA) status

115. A patient has documentation on the discharge summary of urosepsis. The coding staff queries the attending physician about the condition and is provided further information that the patient has septicemia. This is in alignment with the laboratory tests and medication given, but the diagnosis of septicemia was not documented by the physician. How should the physician be requested to document the septicemia?

    a. A brand-new history and physical should be dictated to replace the one in the record.

    b. An addendum to the chart should be written.

    c. The new information should be squeezed in between lines within the progress notes of the last day.

    d. The query sheet will be sufficient to document this information.

Domain 4 *CDI Metrics and Statistics*

Use the chart to answer questions below.

| MS-DRG | 2021 PNEUMONIA DENIAL REPORT | | | | |
	MS-DRG Description	MS-DRG Weight	Denial Total	Agree with Denial	Appeal Denial
193	SIMPLE PNEUMONIA AND PLEURISY WITH MCC	1.3120	30	3	27
194	SIMPLE PNEUMONIA AND PLEURISY WITH CC	0.8639	20	1	19
195	SIMPLE PNEUMONIA AND PLEURISY WITHOUT CC/MCC	0.6658	2	0	2

116. ABC Hospital has a blended rate of $1,820.00. What is the denial total for DRG 193?

    a. $71,635.20

    b. $2,387.84

    c. $47,756.80

    d. $4,775.68

117. What is the total amount ABC Hospital has listed to appeal for DRG 193?

    a. $71,635.20

    b. $65,000.20

    c. $64,471.68

    d. $70,218.36

118. Which DRG has no complications or comorbidities coded?

    a. 193

    b. 194

    c. 195

    d. None listed

Use the chart to answer the questions below.

Quarterly Query Response				
	Month	Query Total	Total Queries Answered	Query Response Rate
1ST QTR	JAN	0	0	0
	FEB	0	0	0
	MAR	0	0	0
2ND QTR	APR	30	10	33
	MAY	35	10	28
	JUN	40	15	37
3RD QTR	JUL	33	20	60
	AUG	34	10	29
	SEP	29	20	69
4TH QTR	OCT	20	15	75
	NOV	15	10	66
	DEC	15	9	60

119. Based on the data above, which quarter had the best response rate?

   a. 1st

   b. 2nd

   c. 3rd

   d. 4th

Use the chart to answer questions below.

Facility Blended Rate: $3,850.00

Billed DRG		DRG Wt.	Revised DRG		DRG Wt.	Total Agree with Denial	Total Denials	Total Charts Reviewed
682	RENAL FAILURE W MCC	1.4866	683	RENAL FAILURE W CC	0.8949	5	12	30
637	DIABETES W MCC	1.3957	638	DIABETES W CC	0.8760	9	25	30

ABC hospital has received denials on DRGs 682 and 637. After review, the denial team agrees with the denials.

120. What is the denial rate for DRG 682?

   a. 12 percent

   b. 25 percent

   c. 83 percent

   d. 40 percent

121. What is the denial rate for DRG 637?

    a. 12 percent

    b. 25 percent

    c. 83 percent

    d. 40 percent

122. What is the DRG payment for DRG 682?

    a. $5,723.41

    b. $5,732.41

    c. $3,500.00

    d. $1,487.00

123. What is the DRG payment for DRGH 683?

    a. $5,723.41

    b. $3,455.37

    c. $3,500.00

    d. $8,949.00

124. What is the overall financial impact for DRG 682 denial?

    a. $3,850.00

    b. $17,1702.30

    c. $10,3021.38

    d. $68,680.92

Use the chart to answer questions below.

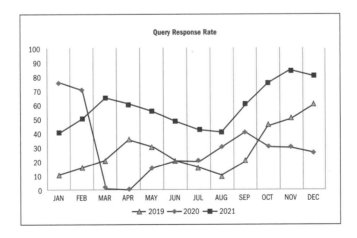

125. The CDI program at Uno Hospital started in January 2019. Ally noticed the seasonal query response rate was low prior to the pandemic in 2020. Based on the line graph above, which summer months have a low query response rate for both 2019 and 2020?

    a. May

    b. June

    c. July

    d. August

126. In what month in 2020 was there a drastic drop in query response?

    a. January

    b. February

    c. March

    d. October

Use the chart to answer questions below.

Key Metric	Quarter 1	Quarter 2	Quarter 3	Quarter 4	Average	Target	% Met
Concurrent record review rate	60%	68%	75%	80%	71%	90%	**79%**
Concurrent physician query rate	40%	45%	50%	40%	44%	40%	**109%**
Physician response rate	40%	30%	30%	50%	38%	80%	**47%**
Physician validation rate	60%	60%	60%	70%	63%	80%	**78%**

127. The CDI leaders at Uno Hospital have been working to meet key metrics for their program. Based on the chart above, which metric is exceeding the target?

    a. Concurrent record review rate

    b. Concurrent physician query rate

    c. Physician response rate

    d. Physician validation rate

128. One of the metrics is trending upward but is still below the target by almost 50%. Which metric is this?

    a. Concurrent record review rate

    b. Concurrent physician query rate

    c. Physician response rate

    d. Physician validation rate

Use the chart to answer questions below.

Physician (Internal Medicine)	Average Patient Severity	LOS
A	2	10.5
B	2	7.1
C	4	7.4
D	2	4

129. The table above shows

    a. No specific trend

    b. Low length of stay with low severity

    c. Increased length of stay with low severity

    d. Severity at target

130. Based on the table above, the profile for physician A may require

    a. Increased review of documentation for query opportunity

    b. Review of reporting

    c. No additional focus

    d. Fewer queries

Domain 5 *Compliance*

131. Based on the AHIMA Code of Ethics, which of the following is not considered an ethical activity?

    a. Coding audits

    b. Using health records for educational purposes within the department

    c. Reviewing the history and physical of a coworker when not part of work assignment

    d. Completion of code assignment

132. Who heads the development of a compliance program?

    a. CDI manager

    b. Compliance officer

    c. HIM director

    d. Privacy officer

133. A CDI manager should include the four components of a compliance plan in their day-to-day operations. These include

    a. Policy and procedure development, Program monitoring, Auditing, and Follow-up

    b. Policy and procedure development, Program monitoring, Auditing, and Billing

    c. Policy and procedure development, Coding, Auditing, and Follow-up

    d. Program monitoring, Coding, Auditing, and Follow-up

134. Alice is ensuring she has all the key components in place for a compliant CDI program. She knows she should have documented, mandatory physician education, and CDI policies and procedures with annual sign-off from all program staff, but what else should she have?

    a. A list of CDI staff

    b. A list of physicians

    c. A detailed query documentation

    d. Documentation of physician advisor

135. Tim knows his manager will be visiting the floor this week to monitor verbally. He needs to make sure he is sharing the clinical evidence from the patient's admission and

    a. He tells the physician exactly what he wants the physician to write

    b. He asks the physician in a non-leading manner

    c. His manager sees him leading the physician to the correct response

    d. He documents the response in the chart for the physician

136. Who should perform the retrospective chart audit of queries?

    a. The CDI that initiated the query

    b. The physician advisor

    c. A fellow CDI staff member

    d. An individual outside of the program operations

137. What is the minimum number of records to pull for a CDI audit?

    a. 20

    b. 25

    c. 30

    d. 1% of all reviews

138. Dani leads all compliance activities for the organization. He is the

    a. Compliance officer

    b. Coding director

    c. CDI officer

    d. Chief medical officer

139. Implementing appropriate clinical documentation practices within an organization

    a. Makes the chart easier to read

    b. Satisfies the objectives of the board

    c. Reduces compliance risk

    d. Helps meet facility goals

140. The CAMP methodology stands for coaching, asking, mastering, and

    a. Problem-solving

    b. Practice

    c. Purpose

    d. Peer learning

PRACTICE EXAM 2

Domain 1   *Clinical Coding Practice*

1. The CPT E/M section of CPT includes new patients and _____ patients.

   a. Clinic

   b. Emergent

   c. Telehealth

   d. Established

2. What is the statement of the symptom, problem, condition, diagnosis, or other factor that is the reason for the encounter (usually by the patient)?

   a. History of present illness

   b. Past medical history

   c. Chief complaint

   d. Diagnosis

3. This is part of the patient history in the health record and is an inventory of body systems obtained through a series of questions designed to elicit signs and/or symptoms.

   a. Past history

   b. History of present illness

   c. Review of systems

   d. Chief complaint

4. What organization develops guidelines for *Current Procedural Terminology* (CPT) use?

   a. World Health Organization

   b. American Medical Association (AMA)

   c. American Health Information Management Association (AHIMA)

   d. American Hospital Association (AHA)

5. What reference terminology is designed to capture clinical information for use in an EHR system?

   a. SNOMED CT

   b. Level II codes

   c. ICD-10

   d. CPT

6. As defined by AHIMA, a descriptive list of names (also called representations or displays), definitions, and attributes of data elements to be collected in an information system or database is a

   a. Data warehouse

   b. Data dictionary

   c. Data set

   d. Data category

7. As defined by AHIMA, a list of recommended data elements with uniform definitions is a

   a. Data warehouse

   b. Data dictionary

   c. Data set

   d. Data category

8. What is the standard performance measure set designed to provide healthcare purchasers and consumers with the information they need to compare the performance of managed healthcare plans?

   a. Uniform Hospital Discharge Data Set (UHDDS)

   b. Healthcare Effectiveness Data and Information Set (HEDIS)

   c. Outcomes and Assessment Information Set (OASIS)

   d. CMS Electronic Clinical Quality Measures (eCQMs)

9. A patient underwent excision of a malignant lesion of the skin of the chest that measured 1.0 cm, and there was a 0.2-cm margin on both sides. Based on the 2022 CPT codes, which code would be used for the procedure?

   a. 11401, Excision, benign lesion including margins, except skin tag (unless listed elsewhere), trunk, arms or legs; excised diameter 0.6 to 1.0 cm

   b. 11601, Excision, malignant lesion including margins, trunk, arms, or legs; excised diameter 0.6 to 1.0 cm

   c. 11602, Excision, malignant lesion including margins, trunk, arms, or legs; excised diameter 1.1 to 2.0 cm

   d. 11402, Excision, benign lesion including margins, except skin tag (unless listed elsewhere), trunk, arms or legs; excised diameter 1.1 to 2.0 cm

10. A 45-year-old man with known AIDS is admitted to the hospital for treatment of HIV-related Pneumocystis carinii pneumonia. What is the principal diagnosis code?

    a. B20

    b. J18.9

    c. B59

    d. Any of the above

11. A patient is admitted to the hospital with shortness of breath and congestive heart failure and subsequently develops respiratory failure. The patient undergoes intubation with ventilator management. The correct sequencing of the diagnoses in this case would be

    a. Congestive heart failure and respiratory failure

    b. Respiratory failure

    c. Respiratory failure and congestive heart failure

    d. Shortness of breath, congestive heart failure, and respiratory failure

12. A patient was admitted with pneumonia. Sputum cultures on day three of admission indicate a Klebsiella pneumonia. What is the present on admission (POA) status for the Klebsiella pneumonia and why?

    a. Y, because the pneumonia was present on admission, even though the organism was not verified until days later

    b. N, because the type of pneumonia was not verified until after admission

    c. U, because the coding professional must query the physician for POA status in this case

    d. W, because the physician cannot tell if the reason for the pneumonia at the time of admission was the Klebsiella or not

13. A patient was admitted with a diagnosis of encephalopathy. The patient was admitted for acute renal failure, dementia, with medication adjustments. The CDI professional issued a compliant query for the cause of the encephalopathy. The physician responded that he was clinically unaware. Based on the physician response, this is POA of?

    a. Y

    b. N

    c. U

    d. W

14. CMS will not pay the Complication or Comorbidity (CC)/Major Complication or Comorbidity (MCC) DRG for those selected hospital-acquired conditions (HACs) coded with a POA indicator of

    a. Y

    b. N

    c. U

    d. W

15. In review of the progress notes, it was noted the patient fell getting out of bed on day 3 of their hospital visit for CVA. She was sent to the surgery for an open reduction and internal fixation (ORIF) of the right hip. Discharge states Femur fracture, right with ORIF. What is the correct POA status?

    a. Y

    b. N

    c. U

    d. W

Use the scenario and chart below for questions 16–18.

The patient was admitted with hip replacement for fracture of the left hip. The patient has a history of hypertension, diabetes Type II, and congestive heart failure. On admission, a Stage III pressure ulcer was noted on the right heel. Wound care consulted. Patient agreed to proceed with surgery.
Discharge diagnoses:

- Fracture of left hip
- Diabetes
- Stage III pressure ulcer heel

MS-DRG	MS-DRG Title	Weights
521	HIP REPLACEMENT WITH PRINCIPAL DIAGNOSIS OF HIP FRACTURE WITH MCC	3.0662
522	HIP REPLACEMENT WITH PRINCIPAL DIAGNOSIS OF HIP FRACTURE WITHOUT MCC	2.1894
533	FRACTURES OF FEMUR WITH MCC	1.4162
534	FRACTURES OF FEMUR WITHOUT MCC	0.7902
535	FRACTURES OF HIP AND PELVIS WITH MCC	1.2328
536	FRACTURES OF HIP AND PELVIS WITHOUT MCC	0.7717

16. Based on the above scenario, what DRG would be billed?

    a. 521

    b. 522

    c. 533

    d. 534

17. What would the expected payment be for the DRG billed above with a blended rate of $5,850.00?

    a. $17,937.27

    b. $12,807.99

    c. $8,284.77

    d. $4,622.67

18. Which diagnosis would be a POA of N (Not Present on Admission)?

    a. Fracture of left hip

    b. Diabetes

    c. Stage III pressure ulcer heel

    d. None of the above

Use the list below for questions 19–20.

- Coreg
- Diovan
- Accupril

19. Which condition does each of the above medications treat?

    a. Infection

    b. Gastritis

    c. Heart failure

    d. Cirrhosis

20. The patient was noted to be hypotensive with BP 101/70. He was treated with _____ for his hypotension.

    a. Amlodipine

    b. Buscar

    c. Nitro-Stat

    d. Levophed

21. A patient taking Sinemet began to experience lethargy and some cognitive changes. The patient was admitted, and the physician diagnosed the patient with secondary encephalopathy due to Sinemet. The CDI professional should construct a compliant query for

    a. The reason the patient is on Sinemet

    b. Toxic encephalopathy

    c. Drug interaction

    d. No query is needed

22. A patient taking Sinemet as directed began to experience lethargy and some cognitive changes. The patient was admitted, and the physician diagnosed the patient with secondary encephalopathy due to Sinemet. Is this coded as a(n)

    a. Adverse effect

    b. Poisoning

    c. Z code only

    d. Sign or symptom

23. In performing CDI review in the clinic, Alice noted the patient diagnosis was stated as chest pain. She had insufficient documentation to assign a more specific code. She would assign a code that is considered as

    a. MCC

    b. NEC

    c. CC

    d. Unspecified

24. This 60-year-old patient with diabetes was admitted and found to have gastroparesis. The patient was treated with Reglan and a jejunostomy tube was placed.

    Discharge Diagnosis:
    • Diabetes Type II
    • Gastroparesis

    How would this be coded?

    a. Diabetes Type II

    b. Gastroparesis

    c. Diabetes with gastroparesis

    d. Diabetes with other specified complication

25. An 88-year-old male was opening a drawer at home and inadvertently moved backwards and had a minor fall. The patient noticed some pain and presented for workup. He was found to have a fracture of the right lower leg. The patient was treated and released with instruction to take meds as prescribed. Discharge diagnoses include fractured tibia, osteoporosis, hypertension, and hypocalcemia. This fracture

   a. Is coded as pathologic with osteoporosis

   b. Will impact hospital quality scores

   c. Is coded as minor

   d. Is coded as a traumatic fracture

26. A patient is being seen in the physician's office for possible pneumonia. He also has shortness of breath. The physician office notes state rule out pneumonia, fatigue, shortness of breath. The patient's reported diagnosis for this outpatient clinic visit should be

   a. Rule out pneumonia

   b. Pneumonia with shortness of breath

   c. Shortness of breath, fatigue

   d. Pneumonia

27. A 60-year-old patient was admitted with cellulitis. The history and physical documented that the patient has a history of hypertension, diabetes, and vertigo about 8 years ago with no recurrence. The patient was treated with IV antibiotics, Novolog, and Tenormin during the hospital stay. What is the appropriate reporting and sequencing of these diagnoses?

   a. Diabetes, cellulitis, hypertension, and vertigo

   b. Cellulitis, diabetes, hypertension, and vertigo

   c. Cellulitis, diabetes, and hypertension

   d. Hypertension, diabetes, and cellulitis

28. The "code, if applicable, any causal condition first" note in the ICD-10-CM Tabular List indicates that this code may be assigned when the causal condition is unknown or not applicable. When the causal condition is known, the code for that condition may be reported as which type of diagnosis?

   a. Comorbidity

   b. Manifestation

   c. Principal

   d. Qualified

29. A patient with COPD is admitted with an acute exacerbation of chronic systolic heart failure. On day three of the admission, the provider documents the patient now is experiencing an acute exacerbation of his COPD. What is the POA indicator for the COPD exacerbation?

   a. Y

   b. N

   c. U

   d. W

30. A Medicare patient admitted as an inpatient with acute abdominal pain is found to have appendicitis and has an appendectomy. The patient has a length of stay of 2 days. Reimbursement will be paid under which classification system?

    a. MS-DRG

    b. APG

    c. RBRVS

    d. APC

31. What factors of the APR-DRG system allow for capturing the extent of the patient's conditions and expected loss of life while an inpatient?

    a. Severity of illness and risk of mortality

    b. Severity of diagnosis and risk of morbidity

    c. Complications and comorbidities

    d. Hospital-acquired conditions and present on admission

32. The CDI specialist has performed a chart review and notes clinical indicators are not sufficient, but the documentation of sepsis is present. The provider was queried and confirms the diagnosis of sepsis is present. This is an example of

    a. Code assignment and clinical criteria

    b. Compliance

    c. Retrospective query

    d. Overburden of the physician

33. CMS developed national correct coding methods that seek to identify improper coding that can lead to improper payments. This is called

    a. Medicare Code Editor (MCE)

    b. National Correct Coding Initiatives Edits (NCCI)

    c. Minimum Data Set (MDS)

    d. None of the above

34. CMS utilizes contractors like recovery audit contractors (RACs), comprehensive error rate testing (CERT) contractors, supplemental medical review contractors (SMRCs), zone program integrity contractors (ZPICs), and unified program integrity contractors (UPICs) to perform what function?

    a. Save CMS dollars

    b. Work with the OIG

    c. Protect the Medicare trust fund

    d. None of the above

35. This type of external review ensures the diagnosis, procedures, and discharge disposition is coded correctly

    a. DRG validation

    b. DRG assessment

    c. DRG accuracy

    d. DRG clinical validation

Use the following scenario to answer questions 36 and 37.

A patient is admitted for a cerebral infarction. Residual effects at discharge include aphasia and dysphagia. The patient developed acute diastolic congestive heart failure while admitted and was treated with Lasix in addition to being given Betapace for his long-standing hypertension.

36. Which condition is considered a major complication comorbidity?

    a. Cerebral infarction

    b. Acute diastolic congestive heart failure

    c. Hypertension

    d. Dysphagia

37. Which condition meets the definition of comorbidity?

    a. Cerebral infarction

    b. Acute diastolic congestive heart failure

    c. Hypertension

    d. Dysphagia

Domain 2   *Education and Leadership Development*

38. ABC Hospital is implementing a new CDI program and have purchased software to assist with workflow from the ED to discharge across multiple facilities. Roni, the CDI manager, wants to dissect implementation into several smaller projects called sprints. This project approach is called

    a. AGILE

    b. SCRUM

    c. CQM

    d. TQM

39. When the scope of a project is not delivered, not completed before the targeted date, or cannot be completed and still budgeted, it is noted as a(n)

    a. Undeliverable

    b. Negative goal

    c. Project failure

    d. Constraint

40. As health information and CDI professionals, we are expected to uphold professional responsibilities, standards, and values in moral dilemmas. This is known as

    a. Moral

    b. Compliant

    c. Ethics

    d. Moral courage

41. Annabella decided it was quicker to develop the query for the provider and complete the response herself within the EHR. This is

    a. Great physician support

    b. Something that will help the provider and the facility

    c. Unethical

    d. Ethical

42. The Compliance Department has reviewed the most recent OIG workplan and has suggested the CDI Department review data to determine trends and identify patterns in the data set. This is called

    a. Data mining

    b. Data trending

    c. Data retrieval

    d. Data risk analysis

43. Medicare is using this technique to identify fraudulent activity through claims review. An example would be a provider billing for services outside of their specialty. What is this called?

    a. Predictive mining

    b. Predictive modeling

    c. Data prediction

    d. Predictive trending

44. In clinical quality management, this is a four-step continual improvement of a product or process:

    a. Plan-do-study-act (PDSA)

    b. Pause-do-study-act (PDSA)

    c. Planning-doing-studying-acting (PDSA)

    d. Plan-do-study-analyze (PDSA)

45. The manager of the CDI team knows their team will be collaborating with physicians and other departments. The new hire on their team has already had three complaints in 4 weeks regarding being nonresponsive and ignoring others. The manager needs to collaborate with her on what?

    a. Making it past the orientation period

    b. Emotions

    c. Being a leader

    d. People skills

46. Which question below would be inappropriate for a CDI new hire interview?

    a. How often are ICD codes updated?

    b. How is CDI important to the organization's revenue cycle?

    c. How can you get us more money on reviews?

    d. When working on a team, what role do you usually take and why?

47. A CDI Assessment Report when starting a new program should include analytics on all *but* one of the following:

    a. Focused MS-DRG review

    b. Reimbursement impact

    c. Target CMI

    d. Physician delinquency analysis

48. The physician leader of a CDI program should have how many hours of training at a minimum?

    a. 20

    b. 30

    c. 40

    d. Dependent on bed size

49. What physician specialty is usually a top priority for a CDI program leader?

    a. Emergency department

    b. Hospitalists

    c. Internal medicine

    d. Community-based

50. A physician CDI training program should involve a training team of

    a. Physician instructors only

    b. Physician instructor and compliance expert

    c. Physician instructor and clinical documentation expert

    d. Physician champions

51. What type of physician should be identified for CDI training?

    a. Attending

    b. Locum tenens

    c. Consultants

    d. Rotating

52. CDI should be a collaborative team effort between the physician, CDIPs, and the

    a. Attending

    b. Coder

    c. Compliance specialist

    d. Medical staff

53. CDI has direct impact on a patient's record and should be

    a. Program-driven

    b. Goal-oriented

    c. Patient-centered

    d. Record-focused

54. Providers should build relationships with payers like primary insurers, Medicare administrative contractors (MACs), and

    a. Office of Inspector General (OIG)

    b. Department of Justice (DOJ)

    c. Quality Improvement Organization (QIO)

    d. PIC

55. Which of the following is a best practice for managing clinical documentation programs?

    a. Keep a low profile

    b. Interrupt the physicians when needed

    c. Query on everything

    d. Know the benchmarks and validate the data regularly

56. The CDI department should provide physicians follow-up education on denials received related to

    a. Documentation issues causing the denials

    b. Payer improvements

    c. Tracking system

    d. Staff concerns

57. What Centers for Medicare and Medicaid Services (CMS) program requires providers to receive an EHR incentive payment for EHR systems?

    a. Merit-Based Incentive Program

    b. Meaningful Use incentive Program

    c. Meaningful Measures

    d. HEDIS Incentive Program

58. Star is the CDI manager at Main Hospital and has been delegated the task of creating the CDI policies and procedures. What should she remember when starting with generic templates?

    a. Remember to leave the procedures listed intact

    b. Make sure they represent industry standards

    c. Customize for the organization

    d. Make sure she and her director agree

59. Veronica, a CDI manager, realizes that one of her long-term employees is experiencing a decrease in her quality. Veronica has counseled the employee several times, and she has documented the issues and placed them in the employee's file. Veronica has been advised by her manager that she needs to initiate a performance improvement plan for the employee. The next step that Veronica needs to do is

    a. Document performance issues

    b. Meet with the employee to review the performance improvement plan

    c. Develop an action plan incorporating SMART goals that will assist the employee in achieving performance goals

    d. Review the performance improvement plan with the HIM manager and human resources

60. The CDI professional is charged with ensuring what?

    a. The facility gets paid more than usual

    b. Ensuring documentation supports the care provided

    c. Increasing quality payments

    d. Increasing patient utilization

61. Dr. Jones is responsible for educating documentation challenges to other physicians in the organization. What type of interaction is this called?

    a. Physician interaction

    b. Peer-to-physician

    c. Peer-to-peer

    d. Physician-to-physician

62. In CDI physician training, the instructor explained CDI involves ensuring accurate coded data and documentation to obtain payment that is correct and legally entitled to the provider. What is this called?

    a. Coding optimization

    b. Upcoding

    c. Fraud

    d. Maximation

63. Ongoing compliance education should be performed for CDI professionals. What education below should be a part of this education?

    a. EHR updates

    b. Encoder updates

    c. DOJ workplan

    d. Review of ICD-10-CM/PCS Official Guidelines for Coding and Reporting

64. When audits are performed by payers or external contractors and overpayments are identified in a small claims sample, the entities can request payment over that entire population, such as DRGs. What is this type of payment adjustment called?

    a. Extrapolation

    b. Recoupment

    c. Account recoup

    d. DRG analysis

65. Queries can be performed on paper, electronically, verbally, close-ended or _____?

    a. In any format

    b. Compliance-ended

    c. Open-ended

    d. In a template

66. When starting a new CDI program basic _____ is(are) essential.

    a. Templates

    b. Software

    c. Education

    d. Staffing

67. The CDI manager and coding manager have asked that claims review be included with the quarterly audit. Why may this be important?

    a. To find DRG mismatch accounts

    b. To look for chargemaster errors

    c. To find issues in claim submission

    d. To monitor billing

Use the chart to answer the questions below.

SURGICAL HIERARCHY	
MDC 06 Diseases and disorders of the digestive system	
326-328	Stomach, esophageal and duodenal procedures
329-331	Major small and large bowel procedures
332-334	Rectal resection
335-337	Peritoneal adhesiolysis
338-343	Appendectomy
344-346	Minor small and large bowel procedures
347-349	Anal and stomal procedures
350-355	Hernia procedures
356-358	Other digestive system O.R. procedures

68. Based on the surgical hierarchy above, a patient that has which procedure in the example is lowest in the hierarchy?

    a. Stomach, esophageal and duodenal procedures

    b. Major small and large bowel procedures

    c. Hernia procedures

    d. Other digestive system O.R. procedures

69. Based on the surgical hierarchy above, a patient that has which procedure in the example is highest in the hierarchy?

    a. Stomach, esophageal and duodenal procedures

    b. Major small and large bowel procedures

    c. Hernia procedures

    d. Other digestive system O.R. procedures

70. A patient had a bypass small intestine to rectum and a removal of artificial sphincter from anus; which is higher in the hierarchy?

    a. Stomach, esophageal and duodenal procedures

    b. Major small and large bowel procedures

    c. Rectal resection

    d. Anal and stomal procedures

71. When the content of the health record is not trustworthy and safe, it is not

    a. Complete

    b. Compliant

    c. Reliable

    d. Accurate

72. Researchers state the reasons and causes of poor-quality clinical documentation include: the importance of physician clinical documentation is not a top priority for healthcare organizations; the information is complex; there are unstructured or inconsistent processes for recording and collection of information, and

    a. It's too hard to comply

    b. Low interest by providers

    c. Not enough staff

    d. Medical school and residency programs do not teach clinical documentation practices

73. The basis of APR-DRGs include severity of illness relates to the extent of physiologic decompensation or organ system loss of function; risk of mortality relates to

    a. The likelihood of dying

    b. Patient risk

    c. Impact of disease

    d. Outcomes of disease process

Domain 3   *Record Review and Document Clarification*

74. Gina has 20 queries that have not been answered by the provider that are past the target date. She should

    a. Retire the queries

    b. Follow the policy on query response

    c. Complete the queries

    d. Forward to physician champion

75. In review of the operative report, the physician documented removal of the sigmoid colon from the descending colon to the rectum. The correct root operation would be

    a. Excision

    b. Resection

    c. Removal

    d. Repair

76. A 32-year-old female with adenocarcinoma of the uterus was admitted for removal. The discharge summary states total removal of uterus. The path report states uterus, tubes, ovaries, cervical tissue, and lymph nodes. The CDI should

    a. Clarify if the cervix was removed

    b. Clarify if the lymph nodes were removed

    c. Clarify if tubes and ovaries were removed

    d. Clarify all of the above

77. In Procedure Coding System (PCS), it may be necessary to query for

    a. Root operation

    b. Body part

    c. Approach

    d. All of the above

78. A physician query is sometimes called a clarification, clinical clarification, or documentation clarification. What is another term used for a query?

    a. Documentation alert

    b. Documentation inquiry

    c. Documentation question

    d. Clarification inquiry

79. What application does the CDI professional utilize to pull a specific set of cases from the EHR for CDI review?

    a. DRAGON

    b. Natural Language Processing (NLP)

    c. 3M

    d. SNOMED

80. Amanda is performing her first review of a procedure note for debridement. What is important to determine to accurately code the procedure?

    a. Whether the debridement is necessary

    b. Where the debridement is performed

    c. Whether debridement is excisional or non-excisional

    d. Whether the debridement is wide

81. A 64-year-old patient was admitted with ischemic stroke. On admission, it appeared the patient was doing well until it was noted the patient was experiencing a change in mood, a headache, and nausea. An MRI was subsequently performed, and a clot was noted, resulting in increased intracranial pressure (ICP). The patient was sent to surgery for thrombectomy to relieve ICP. The CDI professional should generate a compliant query for what diagnosis?

    a. CVA

    b. Migraine

    c. Cause of nausea

    d. Cerebral edema

82. In review of the health record, history and physical (H&P) states admission with shortness of breath, cough with sputum with infiltrate noted on chest x-ray. The physician orders IV Zosyn and albuterol. The history notes state hypertension and COPD currently exacerbated. Labs show elevated WBCs and Klebsiella pneumoniae. The CDI professional should generate a compliant query for what diagnosis?

    a. Hypertension

    b. COPD exacerbation

    c. Pneumonia

    d. Pneumonia with causative organism

83. Abnormal findings (laboratory, x-ray, pathologic, and other diagnostic results) that do not have clinical significance stated by the provider are

    a. Coded as if they are significant because they are listed in the health record

    b. Not coded and reported

    c. Coded as other diagnoses

    d. Cannot be principal

84. A patient was admitted with hypertension, shortness of breath, heart failure, and COPD. Labs show a B-type natriuretic peptide (BNP) of 1200 and a glomerular filtration rate (GFR) of 50. The patient was treated with Lasix. What compliant query should be requested?

    a. Type of hypertension

    b. Type of heart failure and stage of chronic kidney disease

    c. Acute renal failure

    d. Type of heart failure

85. What impacts the complexity of the patient and shows severity of illness and intensity of service in patient care?

    a. Specificity

    b. Quality

    c. Utilization

    d. Location of care

86. This patient is a 62-year-old male with a past medical history of diabetes who presents with right hip fracture after falling at home while getting out of the car following a discharge earlier today for treatment following a fall from a tree with rib fracture and mild bilateral pulmonary contusions. CT head, cervical spine, and abdomen/pelvis and x-rays of bilateral knees and forearm showed no acute fractures or dislocations prior to initial discharge earlier today. What is the POA status of the rib fractures?

    a. Not present on admission

    b. Present on admission

    c. Clinically undetermined

    d. Unknown

87. A 50-year-old patient is admitted for ulcerative colitis and started on Humira and a bland diet. The patient stated some difficulty urinating and is on active surveillance. Patient was discharged with follow-up with urology. This CDI professional queried the provider as shown below.

    Query:
    Patient stated to be on active surveillance. Please document this as prostate cancer.

    This query is

    a. Non-leading and appropriate

    b. Leading and inappropriate

88. Dr. Good asked if he can add a sepsis diagnosis to any patient that has a fever, elevated white blood cells (WBCs), and ordered antibiotics. What should the CDI professional state to Dr. Good?

    a. This will save us time in chart reviews.

    b. This will reduce our need to query.

    c. Please speak with the other hospitalists.

    d. This would be an inappropriate practice.

89. A patient was admitted with a traumatic brain injury (TBI) with no responses. The CDI professional should

    a. Query for the cause of TBI

    b. Query the provider for an explanation of no response and review the record for the Glasgow coma score

    c. Query the provider if coma should be reported and review the record for the Glasgow coma score

    d. Query for type of injury

90. A patient presented to the ED with a fever and WBCs at 14,000 and ketones in urine. The patient was experiencing fatigue and altered mental status, nausea, vomiting, and abdominal pain. On admission, the patient was diagnosed with cystitis. The patient also had elevated blood sugar at 325 and was subsequently admitted. The physician documented diabetes at discharge. Based on the physician documentation, the CDS may want to query for

    a. Bacterial cystitis

    b. Type of organism

    c. Diabetes with ketoacidosis

    d. No query warranted

91. The following query was found in a patient's health record. Which of the answers best applies to this query?

    Dr. Sprout: This patient received IV Azithromycin and Vasopressors; please document sepsis in the progress note to justify the drug administration.

    a. This is a leading query

    b. This query brings in information not documented within the chart and is inappropriate

    c. This is a yes or no query

    d. This is an appropriate query

92. CDI professionals gather additional information for accurate documentation. Which item below would not require a query?

    a. Disease not specified as chronic, acute, or subacute

    b. Duration of back pain

    c. Missing documentation

    d. Left or right ear

93. It is important that coders and CDI professionals not capture diagnoses that are not documented for higher payment. This practice is called

    a. Optimization

    b. Unbundling

    c. Revenue enhancement

    d. Upcoding

94. A physician query would not be required in which of the following cases?

    a. Patient admitted with chest pain and elevated troponins

    b. Patient admitted with abdominal pain with anemia and bright red blood per rectum

    c. Pain in the arm noted on x-ray with no treatment noted

    d. History of chronic obstructive pulmonary disease (COPD) without exacerbation noted on discharge summary and acute COPD stated on admission with order for albuterol

95. In performing daily CDI review, April notes the nursing staff documented the patient's skin integrity on admission and states the presence of a Stage II pressure ulcer. April does not see clear physician documentation stating whether the ulcer was present on admission. What should April do?

    a. Complete as present on admission

    b. Formulate a query to determine if the condition was present on admission

    c. Complete as unknown on admission

    d. Complete as not present on admission

96. When a health record has more than one query generated for one case,

    a. The physician should be alerted

    b. The health record should be generated the next day

    c. Nothing. Records should never have multiple queries

    d. The physician should be called

97. Coding staff primarily query physicians

    a. Concurrently

    b. Retrospectively

    c. Both

    d. Before discharge

98. Severe sepsis includes the signs and symptoms of sepsis plus

    a. Headache

    b. Organ dysfunction

    c. Multi-organ dysfunction

    d. Infection

99. A common documentation issue with encephalopathy is

    a. Documentation of the cause of the encephalopathy

    b. Documentation of the site of the encephalopathy

    c. Documentation of the treatment of the encephalopathy

    d. Inadequate query response

Use the chart below for questions 100–101.

MS-DRG	TYPE	MS-DRG Title	Weights
061	MED	ISCHEMIC STROKE, PRECEREBRAL OCCLUSION OR TRANSIENT ISCHEMIA WITH THROMBOLYTIC AGENT WITH MCC	2.8912
062	MED	ISCHEMIC STROKE, PRECEREBRAL OCCLUSION OR TRANSIENT ISCHEMIA WITH THROMBOLYTIC AGENT WITH CC	1.9883
063	MED	ISCHEMIC STROKE, PRECEREBRAL OCCLUSION OR TRANSIENT ISCHEMIA WITH THROMBOLYTIC AGENT WITHOUT CC/MCC	1.7097
064	MED	INTRACRANIAL HEMORRHAGE OR CEREBRAL INFARCTION WITH MCC	1.9189
065	MED	INTRACRANIAL HEMORRHAGE OR CEREBRAL INFARCTION WITH CC OR TPA IN 24 HOURS	1.0200
066	MED	INTRACRANIAL HEMORRHAGE OR CEREBRAL INFARCTION WITHOUT CC/MCC	0.7116
067	MED	NONSPECIFIC CVA AND PRECEREBRAL OCCLUSION WITHOUT INFARCTION WITH MCC	1.4258
068	MED	NONSPECIFIC CVA AND PRECEREBRAL OCCLUSION WITHOUT INFARCTION WITHOUT MCC	0.8889
069	MED	TRANSIENT ISCHEMIA WITHOUT THROMBOLYTIC	0.7871
070	MED	NONSPECIFIC CEREBROVASCULAR DISORDERS WITH MCC	1.6796
071	MED	NONSPECIFIC CEREBROVASCULAR DISORDERS WITH CC	1.0118
072	MED	NONSPECIFIC CEREBROVASCULAR DISORDERS WITHOUT CC/MCC	0.7717

100. This patient was discharged with a cerebrovascular accident (CVA) with infarct and hemiplegia of dominant side. What DRG would this be assigned?

   a. DRG 62

   b. DRG 65

   c. DRG 66

   d. DRG 71

101. The patient was admitted with possible CVA. The CT and MRI were negative. The MD stated no findings. The discharge diagnosis was stated as TIA. What DRG would this be assigned?

   a. DRG 69

   b. DRG 70

   c. DRG 71

   d. DRG 72

102. What medication below is a thrombolytic agent?

   a. Reac (r-IN)

   b. Retavase (r-PA)

   c. Actin (a-PA)

   d. All of the above

103. Transudative pleural effusion is most common with

    a. Pulmonary disease

    b. Sepsis

    c. Heart failure

    d. Renal failure

104. Malignant pleural effusion is

    a. Malignancy of the pleura

    b. Seen when pleurisy becomes malignant

    c. Sign of bronchitis

    d. Malignant cells in the pleural fluid

105. In reviewing this diagnosis, it is important to differentiate between delirium and dementia.

    a. Syncope

    b. Mental health conditions

    c. Encephalopathy

    d. Paranoia

Domain 4   *CDI Metrics and Statistics*

Andrea has been the director of the CDI program since it started 2 years ago. She has had the same team for a year. Andrea has started a different approach of how work is assigned and monitoring CDI performance. The CDI team should be reviewing 80% of the Medicare discharges daily. Answer the questions below related to the chart.

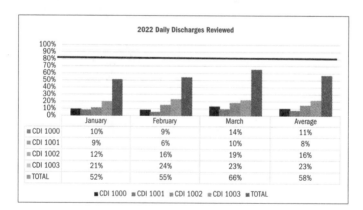

	January	February	March	Average
■ CDI 1000	10%	9%	14%	11%
▨ CDI 1001	9%	6%	10%	8%
▨ CDI 1002	12%	16%	19%	16%
▨ CDI 1003	21%	24%	23%	23%
■ TOTAL	52%	55%	66%	58%

106. The CDI team is currently

    a. Meeting the monthly goal

    b. Not meeting the goal but increasing reviews

    c. Not increasing reviews

    d. Meeting their individual goals

107. In reviewing the data, Andrea notes one of her team members has been performing reviews less than the other team members. This is which CDI?

    a. CDI 1000

    b, CDI 1001

    c. CDI 1002

    d. CDI 1003

Andrea has been monitoring the query response rate for two of the independent physicians. The facility has a goal of an 80% response rate for the physicians. Answer the questions below related to the chart.

QUERY RESPONSE RATE

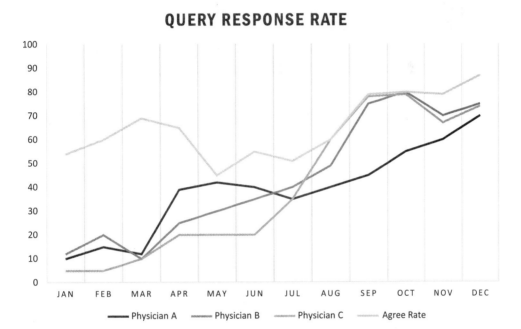

108. Based on the chart above, in what month were all three physicians close to the same range for query responses?

    a. March

    b. June

    c. October

    d. None were within same range

109. Based on the chart above, which physician is showing decreased engagement in response compared to other physicians?

    a. Physician A

    b. Physician B

    c. Physician C

    d. None were within same range

110. In what month did the Agree rate start meeting the goal of 80%?

    a. March

    b. July

    c. September

    d. Goal was not reached

Use the chart below for questions 111–117.

MS-DRG	MS-DRG Title	Weights	No findings	Denial Total	Agree with Denial	Appeal Denial
291	HEART FAILURE AND SHOCK WITH MCC	1.2683	2	10	3	7
292	HEART FAILURE AND SHOCK WITH CC	0.8635	4	7	5	2
293	HEART FAILURE AND SHOCK WITHOUT CC/MCC	0.5899	6	1	0	1

111. Anywhere Hospital has a blended rate of $5,680.00. What is the denial total for DRG 291?

    a. $72,039.44

    b. $34,332.76

    c. $3,350.63

    d. $3,352.76

112. Which DRG did the hospital not agree on any of the denials that were issued?

    a. DRG 291

    b. DRG 292

    c. DRG 293

    d. None

113. CDI programs are effective when they include policies and procedures. What else ensures the program is effective?

    a. Dashboards

    b. Physicians

    c. Nursing staff

    d. Key metrics

114. A CDI program should display metrics in a variety of ways to help identify any issues with the program. Providers should review core metrics. What other type of metrics that are more defined should be identified for monitoring?

    a. Team

    b. Data

    c. Operational

    d. Program

115. Strategic key metrics are used primarily by the executive team. They include quality, profitability, physician satisfaction, and patient satisfaction. These areas are important to monitor for what reason?

    a. To ensure the manager is performing

    b. To make business decisions

    c. To ensure physicians are documenting

    d. For yearly performance bonuses to leaders

116. What is tracked by providers as an indicator of average reimbursement per patient and correlates to revenue and profit and is impacted by coding and CDI?

    a. MS-DRG

    b. DRG weight

    c. Metrics

    d. Case Mix Index (CMI)

117. Anywhere Hospital has noted a decline in the case mix over the past quarter. It is important for leaders to do what?

    a. Determine if there is a change in patient mix, such as a surgical case mix

    b. Find out what CDI is missing

    c. Contact the coding manager on what changes were made

    d. Ask the physician champion to follow up with physicians

Use the chart below for questions 118–122.

Quarterly Query Response			
	Month	Query Total	Query Response Rate
1ST QTR	JAN	58	62
	FEB	55	54
	MAR	60	68
2ND QTR	APR	70	75
	MAY	65	74
	JUN	50	65
3RD QTR	JUL	80	60
	AUG	75	51
	SEP	70	50
4TH QTR	OCT	75	65
	NOV	72	60
	DEC	60	69

118. Based on the data above, which quarter had the best response rate?

    a. 1st

    b. 2nd

    c. 3rd

    d. 4th

119. What should a coder/CDI professional match report be utilized for?

    a. CDI learning opportunities

    b. Coding learning opportunities

    c. Sharing with leadership

    d. Both CDI and coding learning opportunities

120. For reporting of the actual CMI, providers may want to exclude OB, newborn, psychiatry, and what other area?

    a. Rehab

    b. Transitional care

    c. Intensive care

    d. One-day stays

121. Some cases may be removed from CDI MCC monitoring due to minimal CDI professional impact. What cases could be excluded?

    a. Transplants

    b. Tracheostomies

    c. Ventilators

    d. All of the above

122. Data reported by providers related to the CMS value-based purchasing program is shared through what entity?

    a. HCUP

    b. HEDIS

    c. Hospital Compare

    d. Leapfrog

Use the chart below for questions 123–125.

Key Metric	Quarter 1	Target
Concurrent record review rate	70%	90%
Concurrent physician query rate	30%	80%
Physician response rate	50%	80%
Physician validation rate	80%	80%

123. In the chart above, the CDI department is reviewing 70% of the records but may need CDI staff education in what area?

    a. Concurrent record review rate

    b. Concurrent physician query rate

    c. Physician response rate

    d. Physician validation rate

124. The physician validation rate is at 100% of the target. As a CDI manager, you may want to

    a. Congratulate the team

    b. Follow up with CDI team

    c. Perform a query review for leading queries

    d. Nothing additional

125. How is the CDI query rate calculated?

    a. Dividing the daily census by number of records reviewed

    b. Dividing the DRGs for the population by number of DRGs

    c. Dividing the number of records that were queried by the total number of records reviewed

    d. Dividing inpatient stays greater than 1 day by the total records reviewed

Domain 5 *Compliance*

126. A useful corrective action plan includes:

    a. MS-DRG review

    b. SMART goals

    c. Outreach to training team

    d. Focused follow-up education

127. Post-training tests can be important in a compliance program. How does documented education help show compliance?

    a. Shows exam was developed and given

    b. Allows you to develop your program and execute

    c. Shows that the correct direction, support, and tools were provided

    d. Allows the facility to maintain compliance accreditation

128. Anywhere Hospital has a new EHR. The compliance department has informed the system to be aware of compliance risk by the system with

    a. New templates

    b. Alerts

    c. The longitudinal record

    d. Point and click navigation

129. The physicians have recently been trained so they can easily copy documentation from prior visits and bring them to the current visit. This practice can create documentation risks. What is this practice called?

    a. Duplication

    b. Revision

    c. Cloning

    d. Transfer

130. A CDI program should have a comprehensive retrospective review of validity of queries generated, validity of working DRG assignment, validity of a CDI specialist's assignment, and missed query opportunities at least

    a. Monthly

    b. Quarterly

    c. Yearly

    d. Twice a year

131. Medicare has how many levels in the appeals process?

    a. II

    b. III

    c. IV

    d. V

132. The billing department has requested that copies of patients' final coding summaries with associated code meanings for Medicare be printed remotely in the admission department. Currently, they only request the summaries when there is an unspecified procedure. On previous visits to the admission department, the coding supervisor has found the coding summaries were left on a table near the patient entrance. Of the actions presented here, what would be the best action for the coding supervisor to take?

    a. Comply with the request

    b. Refuse to undertake this without further explanation

    c. Ignore the request

    d. Explain to the billing department supervisor that leaving the coding summary in public view violates the patient's right to privacy

133. The federal law that seeks to protect governmental programs from fraud by individuals and companies is

    a. Health Insurance Portability and Accountability Act (HIPAA)

    b. Federal False Claims Act

    c. Deficit Reduction Act of 2005

    d. Tax Relief and Health Care Act of 2006

134. When a person within an organization reports knowledge of fraudulent activities occurring within an organization, he or she is a(n)

    a. Tipster

    b. Whistleblower

    c. Assailant

    d. Defendant

135. Three key compliance components of a CDI program include CDI policies and procedures, documented, mandatory physician education, and

    a. Detailed query education

    b. Goals that are team developed

    c. Staffing for 100% review

    d. Multiple physician leaders

136. The CDI manager has noted two of the physicians have had a 0% agree rate over the past 6 months. The compliance manager should

    a. Assign the CDI specialist other reviews

    b. Speak to the physicians

    c. Begin corrective action

    d. Follow policy and procedures

137. In a recent audit, it was determined there may be over-reporting of sepsis. This area should be included in a(n)

    a. Policy review

    b. External education

    c. Corrective action plan

    d. Suspension

138. This document is an overview of the stay of the patient. Many times providers are scrutinized for components of this document. What is it called?

    a. History and physical

    b. Consultation

    c. Progress note

    d. Discharge summary

139. The health record should include information to justify admission and continued hospitalization, show patient progress/response to treatment, and

    a. Quality of care

    b. Therapy and management

    c. Support of the diagnosis

    d. Care coordination

140. The Conditions of Participation state health records should have final diagnosis with completion of health records

   a. At discharge

   b. Within 30 days

   c. Prior to follow-up visit

   d. As soon as possible

ANSWER KEY 1

Practice Exam 1

1. **c.** The cholecystitis with cholecystectomy should not be coded as an active condition; it is a history of the condition. Do not code conditions that were previously treated and no longer exist. However, history codes (categories Z80–Z87) may be used as secondary codes if the historical condition or family history has an impact on current care or influences treatment (CMS, *ICD-10-CM Official Guidelines for Coding and Reporting*, 2023).

2. **a.** Benign prostatic hypertrophy should be the first listed. 1. Outpatient surgery: When a patient presents for outpatient surgery (same-day surgery), code the reason for the surgery as the first-listed diagnosis (reason for the encounter), even if the surgery is not performed due to a contraindication. 2. Observation stay: When a patient is admitted for observation for a medical condition, assign a code for the medical condition as the first-listed diagnosis. When a patient presents for outpatient surgery and develops complications requiring admission to observation, code the reason for the surgery as the first reported diagnosis (reason for the encounter), followed by codes for the complications as secondary diagnoses (CMS, *ICD-10-CM Official Guidelines for Coding and Reporting*, 2023).

3. **b.** Because the hypertension and diabetes are chronic, they may be coded and reported as many times as the patient receives treatment and care for the condition(s) (CMS, *ICD-10-CM Official Guidelines for Coding and Reporting*, 2023).

4. **c.** The pneumonia or the acute renal failure could be assigned as principal. Two or more diagnoses that equally meet the definition for principal diagnosis in the unusual instance when two or more diagnoses equally meet the criteria for principal diagnosis as determined by the circumstances of admission, diagnostic workup, and/or therapy provided, and the Alphabetic Index, Tabular List, or another coding guidelines does not provide sequencing direction, any one of the diagnoses may be sequenced first (CMS, *ICD-10-CM Official Guidelines for Coding and Reporting*, 2023).

5. **b.** The respiratory failure can be determined by a partial pressure of oxygen (PaO2) < 60 mmHg with a normal or decreased partial pressure of carbon dioxide (PaCO2). Treatment of respiratory failure should be directed towards the underlying cause while providing support with oxygenation and ventilation, as needed (Shebl, Sankat, and Burns 2022).

6. **a.** MI is characterized by presenting with chest discomfort or pressure that can radiate to the neck, jaw, shoulder, or arm. It can be associated with ECG changes and elevated biochemical markers; cardiac troponins (Ojha and Dhamoon 2022).

7. **d.** A lactic acid test is utilized in the diagnosis of sepsis (MedlinePlus, "Lactic Acid Test").

8. **b.** A code from category M80, not a traumatic fracture code, should be used for any patient with known osteoporosis who suffers a fracture, even if the patient had a minor fall or trauma, if that fall or trauma would not usually break a normal, healthy bone (CMS, *ICD-10-CM Official Coding Guidelines for Coding and Reporting*, 2023, Section I.C.13.C).

9. **a.** A code from category M80, not a traumatic fracture code, should be used for any patient with known osteoporosis who suffers a fracture, even if the patient had a minor fall or trauma, if that fall or trauma would not usually break a normal, healthy bone (CMS, *ICD-10-CM Official Coding Guidelines for Coding and Reporting*, 2023, Section I.C.13.C).

10. **c.** When a patient is admitted with respiratory failure and another acute condition (e.g., myocardial infarction, cerebrovascular, aspiration pneumonia), the principal diagnosis will not be the same in every situation (CMS, *ICD-10-PCS Official Guidelines for Coding and Reporting*, 2023, Section I.C.10.b.3).

11. **c.** The AMA publishes the *Current Procedural Terminology* (CPT). CPT is updated annually on January 1 (Oachs and Watters 2020, 152).

12. **d.** SNOMED CT is currently being used in EHR systems as a clinical reference terminology to capture data for problem lists and patient assessments at the point of care. It also supports alerts, warnings, or reminders used for decision support (Oachs and Watters 2020, 158).

13. **d.** These are codes with "in diseases classified elsewhere." In the code title, titles are a component of the etiology/manifestation convention. The code title indicates that it is a manifestation code. "In diseases classified elsewhere" codes are never permitted to be used as first-listed or principal diagnosis codes. They must be used in conjunction with an underlying condition code, and they must be listed following the underlying condition (CMS, *ICD-10-CM Official Coding Guidelines for Coding and Reporting*, 2023, Section I.A.13).

14. **c.** When "with" appears in a code title in the Alphabetic Index (either under a main term or subterm), or an instructional note in the Tabular List, the classification presumes a causal relationship between the two conditions linked by these terms in the Alphabetic Index or Tabular List (CMS, *ICD-10-CM Official Coding Guidelines for Coding and Reporting*, 2023, Section I.A.15).

15. **a.** Official coding guidelines state "the assignment of a diagnosis code is based on the provider's diagnostic statement that the condition exists. The provider's statement that the patient has a particular condition is sufficient. Code assignment is not based on clinical criteria used by the provider to establish the diagnosis." Remember CDI and coding involves reviewing the entire chart and taking all documentation into account (CMS, *ICD-10-CM Official Coding Guidelines for Coding and Reporting*, 2023, Section I.A.19, 12).

16. **c.** The diagnosis of COVID is stated by the physician even though test is negative. "Code only a confirmed diagnosis of the 2019 novel coronavirus disease (COVID-19) as documented by the provider, or documentation of a positive COVID-19 test result. For a confirmed diagnosis, assign code U07.1, COVID-19. This is an exception to the hospital inpatient guideline Section II, H. In this context, 'confirmation' does not require documentation of a positive test result for COVID-19; the provider's documentation that the individual has COVID-19 is sufficient" (CMS, *ICD-10-CM Official Coding Guidelines for Coding and Reporting*, 2023, Section I.C.g.1a, 27).

17. **b.** G20, Parkinson's is the etiology, and F02, dementia, is considered the manifestation. In the Alphabetic Index, code G20 is listed first, followed by code F02.8X in brackets. Etiology is the cause of the disease (CMS, *ICD-10-CM Official Coding Guidelines for Coding and Reporting*, 2023).

18. **c.** Amlodipine treats hypertension (RxList.com).

19. **b.** Cefepime is being used for symptoms consistent with sepsis (MedlinePlus, "Sepsis").

20. **c.** Spiriva is a bronchodilator (RxList.com).

21. **d.** Edema is a common sign of CHF (MedlinePlus, "Heart Failure").

22. **d.** None of the above. The patient has symptoms consistent with liver disorder (MedlinePlus, "Jaundice").

23. **b.** Lantus is a long-acting insulin (RxList.com).

24. **d.** Both a and b are used to treat Alzheimer's dementia (RxList.com).

25. **c.** Malnutrition should be queried (AHIMA, "Ensuring Compliant Malnutrition Coding").

26. **a.** Medications listed are ACE inhibitors (RxList.com).

27. **c.** Insomnia can be treated with Ambien (RxList.com).

28. **b.** Albumin is found in liver function tests and CMP (MedlinePlus, "Albumin Blood Test").

29. **c.** Lactic acid is used in Sep-3 (Endicott 2016).

30. **c.** Watchful waiting can be used to observe progression of a disease or illness (CDC, "How Is Prostate Cancer Treated?").

31. **a.** The physician principally responsible for the patient's hospital care generally dictates the discharge summary. Regardless of who documents it, the attending physician is responsible for the content and quality of the summary and must date and sign it (Jenkins 2017, 155–156).

32. **b.** A pathology report is a document that contains the diagnosis determined by examining cells and tissues under a microscope. The report may also contain information about the size, shape, and appearance of a specimen as it looks to the naked eye (Reynolds and Morey 2020, 115).

33. **d.** Ventilator-associated pneumonia (CDC, "Ventilator-Assisted Pneumonia").

34. **b.** Congestive heart failure (MedlinePlus, "Heart Failure").

35. **c.** Grand mal (MedlinePlus, "Seizures").

36. **d.** Neutropenia (Territo 2022).

37. **a.** Peripheral arterial disease (PAD) (CDC, "Peripheral Arterial Disease [PAD]").

38. **c.** Ms. Jones is most likely taking Remicade (RxList.com).

39. **b.** Lovenox is an anticoagulant (RxList.com).

40. **d.** Lyrica is an anti-epileptic and also used to treat diabetic neuropathy (RxList.com).

41. **d.** The discharge summary is a summary of event that occurred during hospital visit (Hess, 18).

42. **b.** The American Hospital Association is not a cooperating party (CMS, *ICD-10-CM Official Coding Guidelines for Coding and Reporting*, 2023, 1).

43. **a.** MS-DRGs are within a Major Diagnostic Category (MDC) (CMS, "MS-DRG Classifications and Software").

44. **b.** Determining how often MCCs and CCs are coded is the capture rate (Hess 2015, 85).

45. **a.** Chronic cough. Outpatient coding guidelines do not allow coding of possible conditions as a diagnosis for the patient. Do not code diagnoses documented as "probable," "suspected," "questionable," "rule out," "working diagnosis," or other similar terms indicating uncertainty. Rather, code the condition(s) to the highest degree of certainty for that encounter or visit, such as symptoms, signs, abnormal test results, or other reasons for the visit (Schraffenberger and Palkie 2020, 105).

Domain 2 *Education and Leadership Development*

46. **c.** The governance or oversight committee of a CDI program should be composed of members of executive management, the physician advisor or leader for clinical documentation and CDI, and the manager of the CDI program (Hess 2015, 105).

47. **a.** Ethics is the study of morality using the principles, theories, and decision-making frameworks of philosophy (Oachs and Watters 2020, 886).

48. **c.** The physician leader for CDI should have experience and expertise consistent with the responsibilities demanded by the CDI program (Oachs and Watters 2020, 122).

49. **a.** The CDI program leader should report directly to the CMO, but this is dependent on the organization (Oachs and Watters 2020, 122).

50. **d.** Gaining support of the medical staff is one of the most essential roles of the oversight committee (Hess 2015, 105).

51. **b.** The operations committee should meet weekly during the first few months of the program. There are a number of activities the committee needs to coordinate, and these weekly meetings help facilitate them (Hess 2015, 105).

52. **a.** Key CDI stakeholders include HIM and coding departments, case management and utilization review, medical staff and provider leadership, executive leadership, patient financial services or billing, finance and revenue cycle, quality and risk management, nursing, and compliance and ethics (AHIMA, *Clinical Documentation Improvement Toolkit*, 6).

53. **b.** Any successful program operates by utilizing clearly defined goals and measurements. Some examples of CDI goals include obtaining clinical documentation that captures the patient severity of illness and risk of mortality; identifying and clarifying missing, conflicting, or nonspecific provider documentation related to diagnoses and procedures; supporting accurate diagnostic and procedural coding; MS-DRG assignment, leading to appropriate reimbursement; promoting health record completion during the patient's course of care, which promotes patient safety; improving communication between physicians and other members of the healthcare team; providing awareness and education; improving documentation to reflect quality and outcome scores; and improving coding professionals' clinical knowledge (AHIMA, *Clinical Documentation Improvement Toolkit*, 6).

54. **c.** Key performance indicators (KPIs) should be tracked and trended. The results demonstrate that the goals and benefits of the program are being achieved. It also provides insight into patient care data and profiles (AHIMA, *Clinical Documentation Improvement Toolkit*, 7).

55. **a.** Queries are made a permanent part of the record in some organizations. This makes the query discoverable for review (AHIMA, *Clinical Documentation Improvement Toolkit*, 7).

56. **c.** Clinical and leadership experience for the CDI program is provided by the physician advisor (AHIMA, *Clinical Documentation Improvement Toolkit*, 12).

57. **b.** Retrospective audit is performed of records previously billed to determine deficiencies in documentation and coding for opportunities (AHIMA, *Clinical Documentation Improvement Toolkit*, 14).

58. **d.** Providers should have a policy in place on how to manage unanswered queries. This policy should have minimal impact on the final coding and billing process (AHIMA, *Clinical Documentation Improvement Toolkit*, 17).

59. **b.** When a query remains unanswered, it can be addressed by being designated as an incomplete chart and be subject to the same rules for delinquency and suspension, forwarded to the physician advisor for direct follow-up with the physician, or forwarded through the medical peer review QA process (AHIMA *Clinical Documentation Improvement Toolkit*, 17).

60. **c.** Orientation; the new CDI should undergo department-specific training that is complete and comprehensive. There should be clear objectives for training and can last 90 days to up to 1 year (AHIMA, *Clinical Documentation Improvement Toolkit*, 20).

61. **d.** The CDI supervisor/manager should meet with new staff and inform them of their progress, identify learning needs, and check off items that are completed or closed. Much of their learning will occur with staff and physician interaction on the floor (AHIMA, *Clinical Documentation Improvement Toolkit*, 20).

62. **c.** Having policies and procedures are essential for a good CDI program. Written policies and procedures support operational efficiency and reduce compliance risk (Hess 2015, 242).

63. **b.** The CDI query paper trail helps to support the organization in the investigation or audit process. The paper trail shows why the query was asked, how the physician responded, and how the query was asked. How a query is asked can be scrutinized (Hess 2015, 242).

64. **c.** CDI can impact many departments within the revenue cycle. Important feedback loops for CDI are HIM, compliance, and denials management (Hess 2015, 243).

65. **d.** The attending physician should be queried to confirm the final diagnosis (CMS, *ICD-10-CM Official Guidelines for Coding and Reporting*, 2023, Section III, 104–105).

66. **b.** CDI concurrent review should be performed on day 2 of admission. This allows more documentation to be complete (Hess 2015, 175).

67. **b.** If the new physician advisor does not have CDI expertise, an external physician can be brought in to educate the new physician advisor (Hess 2015, 123).

68. **a.** A mission statement sets the purpose and the philosophy of an organization (Hess 2015, 198).

69. **d.** Facilitating the development of the vision statement of a CDI program is the responsibility of the chair of the CDI steering committee (Hess 2015, 197).

70. **b.** Benefits of an outpatient CDI program: improved quality of clinical documentation, improved charge capture, improved care coordination (Hess 2015, 202).

71. **a.** Knowledge of *International Classification of Diseases, 10th Revision, Clinical Modification* (ICD-10-CM) and *Current Procedural Terminology/Healthcare Common Procedure Coding System* (CPT/HCPCS) coding; and *Medicare Program: Outpatient Prospective Payment System* (OPPS) guidelines are required for an outpatient CDI professional (Hess 2015, 248).

72. **d.** An organization should negotiate the statement of work (SOW) for the project and costs for outsourced CDI projects (Hess 2015, 250).

73. **c.** The diagnostic index can be used with the cancer registry data to undertake data quality analysis (Johns 2020, 85).

74. **a.** It is only in the circumstance when the HAC is the only CC/MCC on the patient's account, and does not carry a POA indicator of Y, will there be a loss of an opportunity to capture additional reimbursement (Casto and White 2021, 85).

75. **d.** Ethical coding standards apply to all settings (AHIMA, "Ethical Standards for Clinical Documentation Integrity (CDI) Professionals 2020," https://www.ahima.org/media/r2gmhlop /ethical-standards-for-clinical-documentation-integrity-cdi-professionals-2020.pdf?oid=301868).

76. **a.** The principal procedure by UHDDS definition is for definitive treatment or treatment of a complication (Schraffenberger and Palkie 2022, 93).

77. **c.** AHIMA's Standards of Ethical Coding state in guideline 4.5 that information from previous encounters should not be used to generate a query ("American Health Information Management Association Standards of Ethical Coding [2016 version]," https://bok.ahima.org /CodingStandards#.Y0_tKXbMK3A).

78. **a.** Non-credentialed coding professionals and students are considered as under the umbrella of the term coding professional and, therefore, subject to AHIMA's Standards of Ethical Coding. ("American Health Information Management Association Standards of Ethical Coding [2016 version]," https://bok.ahima.org/CodingStandards#.Y0_tKXbMK3A).

79. **c.** The UHDDS data elements of sex and discharge disposition are also factors in determining some MS-DRGs (Schraffenberger and Palkie 2022, 92).

80. **d.** Ethical Coding Guideline 1.2 states that internal policies may not conflict with the coding rules, conventions, guidelines, etc. of the coding classifications nor with any official coding advice ("American Health Information Management Association Standards of Ethical Coding [2016 version]," https://bok.ahima.org/CodingStandards#.Y0_tKXbMK3A).

81. **b.** Under HITECH, when there has been unauthorized access or disclosure of protected health information, a breach is found to have occurred (Rinehart-Thompson 2017b, 250–251).

82. **c.** HCCs are not considered in MS-DRG assignment (Hessb, 41)

83. **a.** Healthgrades is utilized to display provider profile data (Hess, 77)

84. **a.** The UHDDS item 11-b defines other diagnoses as "all conditions that coexist at the time of admission, that develop subsequently or that affect the treatment received or the length of stay" (CMS 2021a, Section III, 104–105).

Domain 3 *Record Review and Document Clarification*

85. **c.** Simple pneumonia and pleurisy without cc or mcc should be assigned as the MS-DRG. Pneumonia is listed as the principal with no MCCs or Cs listed (CMS, *ICD-10-CM/PCS MS-DRG* v40.0 *Definitions Manual*).

86. **b.** The attending physicians are responsible for the documentation that supports the final diagnostic statement for the patient (42 CFR § 412.46). The attending physician should be asked to provide the final documented response when inconsistencies arise within the record (CFR, "Medical Review Requirements"; Hess 2015, 28).

87. **b.** CMS defines conditions like fat embolism and Stage III and IV pressure ulcers that are not present on admission to the hospital as hospital-acquired conditions. "For discharges occurring on or after October 1, 2008, hospitals will not receive additional payment for cases in which one of the selected conditions was not present on admission. That is, the case would be paid as though the secondary diagnosis were not present" (CMS, "Hospital-Acquired Conditions [Present on Admission Indicator])."

88. **c.** CMS Conditions of Participation requires that the history and physical examination (also referred to as H&P) be completed no more than 30 days before or 24 hours after admission and the report must be placed in the record within 24 hours after admission [42 CFR 482.24(4)(i)(A)]. If the history and physical have been completed within the 30 days prior to admission, there must be an updated entry in the health record that documents an examination for any changes in the patient's condition since the original history and physical examination, and this entry must be included in the record within the first 24 hours of admission [42 CFR 482.24(4)(i)(B)] (CFR, "Conditions of Participation for Hospitals"; Oachs and Watters 2020, 110).

89. **d.** Medication administration records (MARs) are maintained by nursing staff for all patients and include medications given, time, form of administration, and dosage and strength. The records are updated each time the patient is given his or her medication. The health record must reflect when a medication is given in error, indicating what was done about it, and the patient's response (Oachs and Watters 2020, 110).

90. **c.** Medicare Part C is Medicare Advantage (Hess 2015, 66).

91. **a.** A complication is a secondary condition that arises during hospitalization and is thought to increase the length of stay (LOS) by at least 1 day for approximately 75 percent of patients. A comorbidity is a condition that existed at admission and is thought to increase the LOS at least 1 day for approximately 75 percent of patients (Oachs and Watters 2020, 228).

92. **a.** Hypovolemic shock (Taghavi, Nassar, and Askari 2022).

93. **b.** Gram negative or aspiration pneumonia (Drugs.com, "Aspiration Pneumonia").

94. **c.** Acute diastolic congestive heart failure (CHF) (MedlinePlus, "Heart Failure").

95. **d.** Ischemic stroke (CDC, "About Stroke").

96. **c.** Alcoholic cirrhosis (MedlinePlus, "Alcoholic liver disease").

97. **b.** A 12-lead EKG showing ST elevation is called a STEMI (Akbar, Foth, Kahloon, and Mountfort 2022).

98. **d.** The record should be queried for clarification due to conflicting documentation. The consult and progress notes state recurrent colitis, and the discharge summary states abdominal pain.

99. **c.** The CDI professional should query for malnutrition.

100. **d.** All of the above. Queries can be performed concurrently, prebill, and retrospectively (Oachs and Watters 2020, 287).

101. **d.** Queries should be performed by professionals trained and educated in the compliant query process, such as coding and CDI professionals (Oachs and Watters 2020, 287).

102. **a.** Leading. Instructing the physician specifically what to document should be avoided and is noncompliant.

103. **c.** Acute and chronic systolic heart failure should be queried (MedlinePlus, "Heart Failure").

104. **b.** The CDI professional should query for acute blood loss anemia due to extreme fatigue, shortness of breath, abdominal pain, and melanic stools.

105. **a.** The CDI professional should consider paraplegia when formulating the query.

106. **b.** The CDI professional should consider COPD with exacerbation when formulating the query.

107. **b.** Both diagnoses meet the definition of principal diagnosis equally, and either may be sequenced first (CMS, *ICD-10-CM Official Guidelines for Coding and Reporting*, 2023, Section II.C, 102; Leon-Chisen 2022, 26–27).

108. **b.** The most challenging query type is for clinical validation and may best be addressed by clinical documentation specialists (AHIMA 2019).

109. **c.** The term urosepsis is a nonspecific term. It has no default code in the Alphabetic Index. Should providers use this term, they must be queried for clarification (CMS, *ICD-10-CM Official Guidelines for Coding and Reporting*, 2023, Section I.C.1.d.1.a.ii, 22).

110. **a.** Query the attending physician regarding the clinical significance of the findings and request that appropriate documentation be provided. This is an example of a circumstance where the chronic condition must be verified. All secondary conditions must meet the UHDDS definitions; it is not clear if COPD does (CMS, *ICD-10-CM Official Guidelines for Coding and Reporting*, 2023, Section III, 104–105).

111. **b.** Based on the documentation that the patient takes an antihypertensive drug (Lisinopril), and blood pressure was monitored throughout the stay, a diagnosis of hypertension may be suspected and of clinical relevance (AHIMA 2019).

112. **c.** Excisional debridement can be performed in the operating room, the emergency department, or at the bedside. Coding professionals are encouraged to work with the physician and other healthcare providers to ensure that the documentation in the health record is very specific regarding the type of debridement performed. If there is any question as to whether the debridement is excisional or non-excisional, the provider should be queried for clarification (Schraffenberger and Palkie 2022, 426–427).

113. **d.** It is acceptable to query regarding the status of the postoperative ileus being a complication or not, based on the documentation. Documentation does not suggest perforation or abscess associated with the diverticulitis, and the nausea is a symptom of the ileus and not separately reportable (AHIMA 2019).

114. **b.** When supported by the documentation and clinical indicators in the health record, a multiple-choice query can provide a new diagnosis as one of the choices. This does not constitute introducing new information into the record (AHIMA 2019).

115. **b.** According to AHIMA documentation guidelines, any additional late entry to the record should be labeled as such, and these addenda should be added if the physician is queried but the associated documentation to support the code assignment is not present in the original record. In this case, it is an addendum (Sayles 2020, 78).

Domain 4   *CDI Metrics and Statistics*

116. **a.** The financial impact is $71,635.20. Multiply DRG 193 Weight * blended rate; 1.3120 * $1,820.00 = 2387.84 * 30 = $71,635.20.

117. **c.** The financial impact is $64,471.68. Multiply DRG 193 Weight * blended rate; 1.3120 * $1,820.00 = 2387.84 * 27 = $64,471.68.

118. **c.** DRG 195 has no complications or comorbidities, as noted in the description.

119. **d.** The 4th quarter had the best response rate. 75 + 66 + 60/3 = 67%

    (Formula for simple statistical equations [the number of times something happened/the number of times it could have happened])

120. **d.** The denial rate for DRG 682 is 40%: (12/30)*100 = 40%. Total denials/Total charts reviewed.

121. **c.** The denial rate for DRG 637 is 83%: (25/30)*100 = 83%. Total denials/Total charts reviewed.

122. **a.** $3,850.00*1.4866 = $5,723.41. Blended rate * DRG Weight.

123. **b.** $3,850.00*0.8940 - $3,445.37. Blended rate * DRG Weight.

124. **c.** $3,850.00*1.4866*30=171,702.30 – $3,850.00*1.4866*12=$68,680.92 = $103,021.38. DRG payment*total charts reviewed – DRG weight * total charts denied = Financial impact.

125. **d.** The summer months of June 2019 and June 2020 have the same query response rate.

126. **c.** In March of 2020, there was a significant drop: 70% to 0% due to the pandemic.

127. **b.** The concurrent physician query rate is exceeding the target of 40% and exceeding the goal at 109% (Hess 2015, 189).

128. **c.** Physician response rate is only meeting 47% of the target. The goal is 80% (Hess 2015, 189).

129. **c.** Physician A has a long length of stay with severity of 2. Continued engagement and education is needed to increase physician participation and understanding (Hess 2015, 189).

130. **a.** Physician may require education on documentation and query response and documentation review by CDI for opportunities (Hess 2015, 189).

Domain 5 *Compliance*

131. **c.** Reviewing the history and physical of a coworker when not part of assigned work is not ethical because the review is not part of designated work. This violates the ethical principle of acting with integrity and behaving in a trustworthy manner (Rinehart-Thompson 2017b, 210).

132. **b.** The compliance officer is the leader of an organization's compliance program (Hess 2018, 207).

133. **a.** The four components of a compliance plan should include: Policy and procedure development; Program monitoring; Auditing; and Follow-up as a part of day-to-day functions (Hess 2018, 208).

134. **c.** Detailed query documentation can protect the hospital and evidentiary support of all activities (Hess 2018, 208).

135. **b.** The CDI manager should observe verbal queries to ensure they are nonleading (Hess 2018, 210).

136. **d.** Qualified individuals who are not involved in the day-to-day operations of the CDI program should perform a retrospective audit (Hess 2018, 212).

137. **c.** The minimum number of records to pull for a CDI audit should be 30. More record reviews may be required dependent on organization size/volumes (Hess 2018, 212).

138. **a.** The compliance officer leads all compliance activities for the organization (Hess 2018, 207).

139. **c.** This can help reduce risk to the organization (Hess 2018, 241).

140. **d.** CAMP method stands for coaching, asking, mastering, and peer learning. It is a structured methodology for educating adults that improves skills and increases the sustainability of the training.

ANSWER KEY 2

Practice Exam 2

Clinical Coding Practice

1. **d.** The CPT E/M section of CPT includes new patients and established patients for office or other outpatient visits (Giannangelo 2018).

2. **c.** The chief complaint statement of the symptom, problem, condition, diagnosis, or other factor that is the reason for the encounter, usually by the patient (Giannangelo 2018).

3. **c.** The review of systems section of a patient history is an inventory of body systems obtained through a series of questions designed to elicit signs and/or symptoms (Giannangelo 2018).

4. **b.** The American Medical Association (AMA) develops and distributes CPT and the CPT guidelines (Giannangelo 2018).

5. **a.** SNOMED is designed to capture clinical information for use in an EHR system to record patient encounters (Giannangelo 2018).

6. **b.** A data dictionary is a descriptive list of names (also called representations or displays), definitions, and attributes of data elements to be collected in an information system or database (Giannangelo 2018).

7. **c.** A data set is a list of recommended data elements with uniform definitions (Giannangelo 2018).

8. **b.** CMS contracted with the National Committee for Quality Assurance (NCQA) to develop the Healthcare Effectiveness Data and Information Set (HEDIS). It is the standard performance measure set designed to provide healthcare purchasers and consumers with the information they need to compare the performance of managed healthcare plans (Giannangelo 2018).

9. **c.** The size of the lesion plus the margins are included in coding the excision. Excised diameter: 1.0 cm + 0.2 cm + 0.2 cm = 1.4 cm (AMA, *CPT 2022 Professional Edition* 2022, 101–105).

10. **a.** Whenever an HIV-positive patient is admitted with an HIV-related condition, the principal diagnosis is B20, followed by additional ICD-10-CM codes for all reported HIV-related conditions (CMS, *ICD-10-CM Official Guidelines for Coding and Reporting*, 2023, Section I.C.1.a.2.a, 19).

11. **a.** Respiratory failure may be listed as a secondary diagnosis if it occurs after admission, or if it is present on admission but does not meet the definition of principal diagnosis. Shortness of breath is a symptom inherent to CHF and therefore is not coded (CMS, *ICD-10-CM Official Guidelines for Coding and Reporting*, 2023, Section I.C.10.b, 52–53).

12. **a.** When a code has multiple clinical concepts, such as an infection and the causative organism, it is appropriate to code it as POA regardless of the fact that the culture results are not known until days after admission (CMS, *ICD-10-CM Official Guidelines for Coding and Reporting*, 2023, Appendix I, 110–115).

13. **d.** The POA status would be "W" as the provider was unable to clinically determine whether the condition was present at the time of inpatient admission (CMS 2022a, "Coding").

14. **b.** CMS will not pay the CC/MCC DRG for those selected HACs coded with a POA indicator of N for Not Present on Admission (CMS 2022a, "Coding").

15. **b.** The correct POA status is N for Not Present on Admission. The fracture occurred after admission from a fall (CMS 2022a, "Coding").

16. **a.** DRG 521 would be billed. See CMS Inpatient Prospective Payment System Final Rule DRG weights and tables, Table 5 (CMS 2022b, "FY 2022 IPPS Final Rule Homepage").

17. **a.** $17,937.27 would be the payment DRG weight times blended rate = DRG payment.

18. **d.** None of the above. All conditions would be POA (CMS, *ICD-10-CM Official Guidelines for Coding and Reporting 2023*).

19. **c.** The medications listed all treat heart failure (RxList.com).

20. **d.** Levophed treats life-threatening hypotension (RxList.com).

21. **b.** The CDI professional should construct a compliant query for toxic encephalopathy, which can be due to drugs (AHA, *Coding Clinic for ICD-10-CM and ICD-10-PCS*, 1st Quarter, 2017, 39).

22. **a.** The encephalopathy due to Sinemet would be coded as an adverse effect of a drug. It was taken as prescribed (AHA, *Coding Clinic for ICD-10-CM and ICD-10-PCS*, 1st Quarter, 2017, 39).

23. **d.** An unspecified code is assigned when there is insufficient documentation to assign a more specific code (CMS, *ICD-10-CM Official Guidelines for Coding and Reporting, 2023*, Section I.A.9b, 9).

24. **c.** It is coded as Diabetes Type II with Gastroparesis. Official Coding Guidelines state "The word 'with' or 'in' should be interpreted to mean 'associated with' or 'due to' when it appears in a code title, the Alphabetic Index (either under a main term or subterm), or an instructional note in the Tabular List. The classification presumes a causal relationship between the two conditions linked by these terms in the Alphabetic Index or Tabular List" (CMS, *ICD-10-CM Official Guidelines for Coding and Reporting, 2023*, Section I.A.15, 11).

25. **a.** This fracture is coded as pathologic with osteoporosis. "A code from category M80, not a traumatic fracture code, should be used for any patient with known osteoporosis who suffers a fracture, even if the patient had a minor fall or trauma, if that fall or trauma would not usually break a normal, healthy bone" (CMS, *ICD-10-CM Official Guidelines for Coding and Reporting, 2023,* Section I.C.13.d).

26. **d.** The shortness of breath and fatigue would be reported for this outpatient visit. Do not code diagnoses documented as "probable," "suspected," "questionable," "rule out," or "working diagnosis" or other similar terms indicating uncertainty. Rather, code the condition(s) to the highest degree of certainty for that encounter/visit, such as symptoms, signs, abnormal test results, or other reason for the visit (CMS, *ICD-10-CM Official Guidelines for Coding and Reporting, 2023,* Section IV.H, 111).

27. **c.** Cellulitis, diabetes, hypertension should be coded with the principal diagnosis of cellulitis, as this was the reason for the admission. The vertigo is not a current condition and would not be coded based on the reporting guidelines for the UHDDS for "other conditions" (CMS, *ICD-10-CM Official Guidelines for Coding and Reporting, 2023*, Section III, 104–105).

28. **c.** "Code, if applicable, any causal condition first" notes indicate that this code may be assigned as a principal diagnosis when the causal condition is unknown or not applicable. If a causal condition is known, then the code for that condition should be sequenced as the principal or first-listed diagnosis (CMS, *ICD-10-CM Official Guidelines for Coding and Reporting, FY 2023*, Section I.B.7, 13–14).

29. **b.** Although the COPD was present on admission, the acute exacerbation was not. Therefore, the POA indicator must be N (CMS 2021, 110–115).

30. **a.** Medicare reimburses inpatient stays based on MS-DRGs (Casto and White 2021, 116–118).

31. **a.** SOI and ROM are the factors that are used in the APR-DRG system to classify how ill a patient is and whether they are expected to die while admitted (Foltz et al. 2016).

32. **a.** Official coding guidelines state under Code Assignment and Clinical Criteria: "The provider's statement that the patient has a particular condition is sufficient. Code assignment is not based on clinical criteria used by the provider to establish the diagnosis. If there is conflicting medical record documentation, query the provider" (CMS, *ICD-10-CM Official Guidelines for Coding and Reporting, 2023,* Section I.A.19, 12).

33. **b.** National Correct Coding Initiatives Edits (NCCI) were developed by CMS to identify improper coding that can lead to improper payments (AHIMA, *CDI and Coding Collaboration in Denials Management Toolkit*, 2018, 7).

34. **c.** CMS utilizes contractors to Protect the Medicare trust fund (AHIMA 2018a, 6).

35. **a.** DRG validation is performed by Medicare contractors to ensure the diagnosis, procedures, and discharge disposition is coded correctly (AHIMA 2018a, 9).

36. **b.** The acute diastolic congestive heart failure is the major complication in this case, since it developed after admission (Schraffenberger and Palkie 2022, 92–93)

37. **c.** The hypertension is the comorbid condition as it was the preexisting condition (Schraffenberger and Palkie 2022, 92–93).

Domain 2 *Education and Leadership Development*

38. **b.** SCRUM is a form of an Agile project method that dissects projects into several units called sprints. This includes a high-level plan for the work that will take place in each of the sprints (Oachs and Watters 2020, 851).

39. **c.** A project failure is a project management term as stated for a project that is not delivered, not completed by target date, and has budget effects (Oachs and Watters 2020, 851).

40. **d.** Moral courage allows us to uphold professional responsibilities, standards, and values in moral dilemmas (Oachs and Watters 2020, 885).

41. **c.** CDI professionals must follow ethical standards. This would be unethical. CDI professionals cannot participate in improper preparation, alteration, or suppression of health record information (AHIMA, "Ethical Standards for Clinical Documentation Integrity [CDI] Professionals 2020").

42. **a.** Data mining is a form of data analytics to discover trends and patterns (Oachs and Watters 2020, 519).

43. **b.** Medicare is utilizing predictive modeling to identify variances and flaws in provider billing (Oachs and Watters 2020, 520).

44. **a.** Plan-do-study-act (PDSA) is a four-step continual improvement of a product or process. It is intended to be a never-ending process (Oachs and Watters 2020, 623).

45. **d.** Interpersonal skills are beneficial for CDI professionals as they work with others to accomplish goals (Oachs and Watters 2020, 658).

46. **c.** The CDI role is multifaceted and from a compliance and ethics perspective this question would be inappropriate (AHIMA, "Ethical Standards for Clinical Documentation Integrity [CDI] Professionals 2020").

47. **d.** Include analytics on target CMI, focused MS-DRGs, and reimbursement impact when performing CDI Assessment for a new program (Hess 2015, 132).

48. **c.** The physician leader should have at least 40 hours of training (Hess 2015, 132).

49. **b.** Hospitalists are usually considered for this role, as they take the role of primary care doctor when a patient is hospitalized (Hess 2015, 146).

50. **d.** Physician instructor and a clinical documentation expert should make up the physician CDI training program for peer and expert support (Hess 2015, 144).

51. **a.** Attending physicians should be included in CDI, as they usually admit patients and are responsible for their treatment (Hess 2015, 146).

52. **b.** The coder, physician, and CDI should work together as a team (Hess 2015, 158).

53. **c.** A CDI program should be patient-centered, as it ensures appropriate documentation in the patient record (Hess 2015, 240).

54. **c.** Providers' financial management team should build a relationship with Quality Improvement Organization (QIO) (Hess 2015, 252).

55. **d.** Knowing the benchmarks and validating the data regularly is a best practice for CDI programs' operational success (Hess 2015, 252).

56. **a.** Physicians should be provided feedback on denials related to documentation issues (Hess 2015, 242).

57. **b.** The meaningful use incentive program allows incentive payment if providers prove they are utilizing their EHR meaningfully with specific requirements (Hess 2015, 258).

58. **c.** CDI policies and procedures should not be generic but should be customized for your organization (Hess 2015, 172).

59. **c.** The second step after documenting employee performance issues is to develop an action plan incorporating SMART goals (Kelly and Greenstone 2020, 195).

60. **b.** Ensuring documentation supports the care provided is a duty of CDI.

61. **c.** A peer-to-peer is a communication that is performed between physician colleagues to build relationships and foster program success (Oachs and Watters, 276).

62. **a.** Coding optimization is supported for CDI and coding programs to ensure quality and accuracy in documentation and payments (Oachs and Watters, 295).

63. **d.** CDI professionals should participate in yearly compliance training that includes inpatient and outpatient code updates (if relevant) (Oachs and Watters, 297).

64. **a.** Extrapolation occurs when a payer or contractor applies a correction in reimbursement across a large number of claims and collects the dollars owed (Oachs and Watters, 297).

65. **c.** Queries can be in closed or open-ended format (Oachs and Watters, 289).

66. **c.** Basic education is necessary in the initial implementation of a CDI program (Hess 2015, 244).

67. **d.** When the claim is submitted, the reviewer should compare all the diagnoses and procedures printed on the bill with the coded information in the health record system. This process will help identify whether the communication software between the health record system and the billing system is functioning correctly. The HIM department should share the results of this comparison with patient financial services and the information technology department (Casto 2018, 238).

68. **d.** Other digestive system O.R. procedures are the lowest in the hierarchy. Since patients can have multiple procedures related to their principal diagnosis during a particular hospital stay, and a patient can be assigned to only one surgical class, the surgical classes in each MDC are defined in a hierarchical order. Patients with multiple procedures are assigned to the highest surgical class in the hierarchy to which one of the procedures is assigned (CMS 2016a; *ICD-10-CM/PCS MS-DRG v39.0 Definitions Manual*, https://www.cms.gov/icd10m/version39.0-fullcode-cms/fullcode_cms/P0001.html).

69. **a.** Stomach, esophageal, and duodenal procedures are the highest in the hierarchy. Since patients can have multiple procedures related to their principal diagnosis during a particular hospital stay, and a patient can be assigned to only one surgical class, the surgical classes in each MDC are defined in a hierarchical order. Patients with multiple procedures are assigned to the highest surgical class in the hierarchy to which one of the procedures is assigned (CMS 2016a).

70. **b.** Patient had a major small and large bowel procedure, which is higher in the hierarchy. Since patients can have multiple procedures related to their principal diagnosis during a particular hospital stay, and a patient can be assigned to only one surgical class, the surgical classes in each MDC are defined in a hierarchical order. Patients with multiple procedures are assigned to the highest surgical class in the hierarchy to which one of the procedures is assigned (CMS 2016a; *ICD-10-CM/PCS MS-DRG v39.0 Definitions Manual*, https://www.cms.gov/icd10m/version39.0-fullcode-cms/fullcode_cms/P0001.html).

71. **c.** When content of the health record is not trustworthy and safe, it Is not reliable (Oachs and Watters, 10).

72. **d.** Providers do not learn documentation practices in schools (Oachs and Watters, 3).

73. **a.** Risk of mortality relates to likelihood of dying (Hess 2015, 52).

Domain 3   *Record Review and Document Clarification*

74. **b.** She should follow policies put in place for the program (Hess 2015, 172).

75. **b.** This would be a resection removal of the entire body part (AHIMA, "Guidelines for Achieving a Compliant ICD-10-PCS Query [2019 Update]").

76. **d.** All of the above. Query if the documentation describes a procedure inconsistent with findings on the pathology report (AHIMA, "Guidelines for Achieving a Compliant ICD-10-PCS Query [2019 Update]").

77. **d.** In PCS, it may be necessary to query for all of the above. The coding guidelines for each character should be reviewed for the development of a query (AHIMA, "Guidelines for Achieving a Compliant ICD-10-PCS Query [2019 Update]").

78. **a.** Queries are sometimes called documentation alerts. This term is commonly used with EHRs (AHIMA, *Clinical Documentation Improvement Toolkit*, 2016).

79. **b.** By running NLP software across "free text," CDI professionals obtain a prioritized work list of cases to review (AHIMA, *Clinical Documentation Improvement Toolkit*, 2016).

80. **c.** The coder or CDI professional must determine if the debridement is excisional or non-excisional (AHIMA, *CDI and Coding Collaboration in Denials Management Toolkit*, 2018a).

81. **d.** The CDI professional should query for cerebral edema based on the scenario with ICP and ischemic stroke (Cook et al. 2020).

82. **d.** The CDI professional should query for pneumonia with organism, as stated in labs (AHIMA, *CDI and Coding Collaboration in Denials Management Toolkit*, 2018a).

83. **b.** The provider must indicate the clinical significance for abnormal findings (laboratory, x-ray, pathologic, and other diagnostic results) to be coded and reported. If the findings are outside the normal range and the attending provider has ordered other tests to evaluate the condition or prescribed treatment, it is appropriate to ask the provider whether the abnormal finding should be added (CMS, *ICD-10-CM Official Guidelines for Coding and Reporting*, 2023, Section III.B., 107).

84. **b.** The provider should be queried to determine type of CHF and stage of CKD. This would result in a combination code and be a major complication/comorbidity (AHIMA, *CDI and Coding Collaboration in Denials Management Toolkit*, 2018a).

85. **a.** Specificity helps show the complexity of the diagnoses being treated and shows how sick the patient is and what services are required for treatment (AHIMA, *CDI and Coding Collaboration in Denials Management Toolkit*, 2018a).

86. **b.** The rib fractures would be present on admission. The patient was discharged and then admitted again the same day. The rib fracture was already diagnosed (CMS, *ICD-10-CM Official Guidelines for Coding and Reporting 2023*, Appendix I, 115).

87. **b.** This query is leading in asking the physician specifically what to document. A leading query is one that is not supported by the clinical elements in the health record or directs a provider to a specific diagnosis or procedure (AHIMA, "Guidelines for Achieving a Compliant Query Practice").

88. **d.** This practice would be inappropriate. Regulations and the CDI Code of Ethics state CDI professionals should never participate in or support documentation practices intended to inappropriately increase payment (AHIMA, "Ethical Standards for Clinical Documentation Integrity [CDI] Professionals 2020").

89. **c.** The patient has no response, thus coma can be queried. The coma scale codes (R40.21- to R40.24-) can be used in conjunction with traumatic brain injury codes (CMS, *ICD-10-CM Official Guidelines for Coding and Reporting 2023*, Section I, 18.e.1, 74).

90. **c.** Diabetes with ketoacidosis should be queried with signs and symptoms listed. Query for clarification should be performed. The generation of a query should be considered when the health record documentation is conflicting, imprecise, incomplete, illegible, ambiguous, or inconsistent, describes or is associated with clinical indicators without a definitive relationship to an underlying diagnosis; includes clinical indicators, diagnostic evaluation, and/or treatment not related to a specific condition or procedure; provides a diagnosis without underlying clinical validation, or is unclear for present on admission indicator assignment (AHIMA, "Guidelines for Achieving a Compliant Query Practice").

91. **a.** When formulating a query, it is unacceptable to lead a provider to document a particular response. The query should not be directing or probing, and the provider should not be led to make an assumption (AHIMA, "Guidelines for Achieving a Compliant Query Practice").

92. **b.** The CDI professional would not normally be required to query how long someone has been in pain (Oachs and Watters 2020, 281).

93. **d.** Upcoding is assigning diagnostic or procedural codes that represent higher payment rates than the services that were provided (Oachs and Watters 2020, 281).

94. **c.** The pain was not addressed or treated per the scenario. The generation of a query should be considered when the health record documentation is conflicting, imprecise, incomplete, illegible, ambiguous, or inconsistent, describes or is associated with clinical indicators without a definitive relationship to an underlying diagnosis; includes clinical indicators, diagnostic evaluation, and/or treatment not related to a specific condition or procedure; provides a diagnosis without underlying clinical validation, or is unclear for present on admission indicator assignment (AHIMA, "Guidelines for Achieving a Compliant Query Practice").

95. **b.** The provider should be queried for the present on admission indicator. The generation of a query should be considered when the health record documentation is conflicting, imprecise, incomplete, illegible, ambiguous, or inconsistent, describes or is associated with clinical indicators without a definitive relationship to an underlying diagnosis; includes clinical indicators, diagnostic evaluation, and/or treatment not related to a specific condition or procedure; provides a diagnosis without underlying clinical validation, or is unclear for present on admission indicator assignment (AHIMA, "Guidelines for Achieving a Compliant Query Practice").

96. **a.** When there are multiple questions for one case, the physician is to be alerted that there is more than one query requiring a response; refer to internal policies as well (Hess 2015, 179).

97. **b.** Coders primarily query during retrospective review of the patient's record, post-discharge (Hess 2015, 179).

98. **c.** Severe sepsis includes the signs and symptoms of sepsis plus multi-organ dysfunction (Hess 2015, 180).

99. **a.** A common documentation issue with encephalopathy is documentation of the cause of the encephalopathy (Hess 2015, 183).

100. **b.** DRG 65 would be assigned. The patient had a CVA with infarct and residual hemiplegia at discharge (CMS, *ICD-10-CM/PCS MS-DRG v40.0 Definitions Manual*).

101. **a.** DRG 69 TIA would be assigned. CVA was ruled out (CMS, *ICD-10-CM/PCS MS-DRG v40.0 Definitions Manual*).

102. **b.** Retavase (r-Pa) is a thrombolytic agent (RxList.com).

103. **c.** Transudative pleural effusion is most common with heart failure (MedlinePlus, "Pleural Effusion").

104. **d.** Malignant pleural effusion is malignant cells in the pleural fluid (Arora and Boster 2022).

105. **c.** It is important to differentiate encephalopathy from delirium and dementia. It can present in a variety of ways and may be due to many factors (AHIMA, *CDI and Coding Collaboration in Denials Management Toolkit*, 2018a, 16).

Domain 4 · *CDI Metrics and Statistics*

106. **b.** The CDI team is not meeting the goal of 80% but is improving at 66% review (Hess 2015, 91).

107. **b.** CDI 1001 is only reviewing 8% of her goal. She may need additional training and education (Hess 2015, 91).

108. **a.** In March all providers were close to the same range, around 10%.

109. **a.** Physician A's response rate started to decrease compared to others in July.

110. c. In September, the program started reaching the 80% goal of Agree with query.

111. a. The denial total for DRG 291 is $72,039.44. (1.2683*10)*5,680.00.

112. c. The hospital appealed all denials for DRG 293.

113. d. To be effective, CDI programs should have policies, procedures, and key metrics. This ensures guidance and measuring are in place (Hess 2015, 171).

114. c. CDI programs should monitor core metrics and operational metrics. Operational metrics may develop as the program matures and leadership identifies areas to monitor (Hess 2015, 190).

115. b. Strategic key metrics help with making strategic decisions for the organization (Hess 2015, 192).

116. d. The CMI is the average DRG relative weight for inpatient cases and is considered an indicator of average reimbursement per patient. This number can be impacted by what is documented and coded (Hess 2015, 192).

117. a. CMI can change for changes related to coding but also patient mix and service lines. CMI should be monitored by service and CC capture rate (Hess 2015, 194).

118. b. The 2nd quarter had the best response rate.

119. d. The CDI and coder mismatch report should be used to educate the coder and CDI (AHIMA, *Clinical Documentation Improvement Toolkit*, 2016, 10).

120. a. To track, actual providers may exclude rehab visits (AHIMA, *Clinical Documentation Improvement Toolkit*, 2016, 10).

121. d. Transplants, tracheostomies, ventilators, and elective orthopedic joint replacements are usually driven by the procedure associated with it and require little to no CDI involvement (AHIMA, *Clinical Documentation Improvement Toolkit*, 2016, 10).

122. c. Hospital Compare is reported by hospitals to meet the requirements of the Medicare Value Based Purchasing program (Oachs and Watters 2020, 27).

123. b. The CDI staff may need education on query practices (Hess 2015, 178).

124. c. The manager may want to review queries to ensure compliance (Hess 2015, 190).

125. c. The query rate is calculated by dividing the number of records that were queried by the total number of records reviewed (Hess 2015, 172).

126. **d.**   A corrective action plan should include focused follow-up education (Hess 2015, 219).

127. **c.**   Post-training texts can show the provider has taken the correct steps in team training (Hess 2015, 220).

128. **d.**   The ease and efficiency of the EHR may result in scenarios where, for example, the physician automatically checks (or does not check) all the boxes in a patient's history and physical report; the healthcare organization must therefore implement processes that include training and auditing to counter these possible risks (Hess 2015, 34).

129. **c.**   Cloned documentation or use of copy and paste can be a compliance risk, and policies and procedures should be developed (AHIMA, "Integrity of the Healthcare Record: Best Practices for EHR Documentation [2013 update]").

130. **c.**   CDI programs should have a comprehensive retrospective review at least yearly to ensure compliance and to achieve goals (Hess 2015, 211).

131. **d.**   There are five levels of appeal in the Medicare Appeal process (AHIMA, *CDI and Coding Collaboration in Denials Management Toolkit*, 2018a, 14).

132. **d.**   Health information should not be left in public view (Rinehart-Thompson 2017b, 257).

133. **b.**   The Federal False Claims Act is a federal law that seeks to protect governmental programs from fraud by individuals and companies (Oachs and Watters 2020, 292).

134. **b.**   A person within an organization reports knowledge of fraudulent activities occurring within an organization (Oachs and Watters 2020, 293).

135. **a.**   Detailed query education is one of the key compliance components of a CDI program (Oachs and Watters 2020, 208).

136. **d.**   The manager should follow department policies (Hess 2015, 172).

137. **c.**   The area should be included in a corrective action plan (Hess 2015, 218).

138. **d.**   The discharge summary contains an overview of the stay of the patient (Hess 2015, 17).

139. **c.**   The health record should also include information to support the diagnoses coded (Hess 2015, 6).

140. **b.**   The Conditions of Participation state health records should have final diagnosis with completion of health records within 30 days (Hess 2015, 7).

REFERENCES

Agency for Healthcare Research and Quality. 2016. "Fact Sheet on Patient Safety Indicators. Toolkit for Using the AHRQ Quality Indicators." https://www.ahrq.gov/sites/default/files/wysiwyg/professionals/systems/hospital/qitoolkit/combined/a1b_combo_psifactsheet.pdf.

Agency for Healthcare Research and Quality. 2022. "Patient Safety Indicators Technical Specifications." July. https://qualityindicators.ahrq.gov/measures/PSI_TechSpec.

Akbar, H., C. Foth, R. A. Kahloon, and S. Mountfort. 2022. "Acute ST Elevation Myocardial Infarction." In *StatPearls* [Internet]. Treasure Island, FL: StatPearls Publishing. https://www.ncbi.nlm.nih.gov/books/NBK532281/.

American Health Information Management Association (AHIMA). n.d. "Ensuring Compliant Malnutrition Coding." https://library.ahima.org/doc?oid=105044#.Y3tqGHbMKM8.

American Health Information Management Association (AHIMA). 2011. "Understanding Governmental Audits." *Journal of AHIMA* 82, no. 7: 50–55. https://library.ahima.org/PB/GovernmentAudits#.Y3LIpeTMLg4. (Updated 2013).

American Health Information Management Association (AHIMA). 2013a. "Guidance on a Compliant Query: Internal Escalation Policy." https://bok.ahima.org/doc?oid=301705#.Y3LNVOTMLg4.

American Health Information Management Association (AHIMA). 2013b. "Guidelines for Achieving a Compliant Query Practice." *Journal of AHIMA* 84, no. 2: 50–53.

American Health Information Management Association (AHIMA). 2013c. "Integrity of the Healthcare Record: Best Practices for EHR Documentation (2013 update)." https://library.ahima.org/doc?oid=300257#.Y3fbU3bMKM8.

American Health Information Management Association (AHIMA). 2015. *Clinical Documentation Improvement (CDI) Academy*. Chicago: AHIMA.

American Health Information Management Association (AHIMA). 2016. *Clinical Documentation Improvement Toolkit*. Chicago: AHIMA.

American Health Information Management Association (AHIMA). 2018a. *CDI and Coding Collaboration in Denials Management Toolkit*. Chicago: AHIMA.

American Health Information Management Association (AHIMA). 2018b. *Outpatient Clinical Documentation (CDI) Toolkit*. Chicago: AHIMA.

American Health Information Management Association (AHIMA). 2019. "Guidelines for Achieving a Compliant Query Practice (2019 update)." https://bok.ahima.org/doc?oid=302673#.Y0hJBkzMJjs.

American Health Information Management Association (AHIMA). 2020. "Ethical Standards for Clinical Documentation Integrity (CDI) Professionals 2020." https://www.ahima.org/media/r2gmhlop/ethical-standards-for-clinical-documentation-integrity-cdi-professionals-2020.pdf?oid=301868.

American Health Information Management Association (AHIMA) Work Group. 2015. "Best Practices in the Art and Science of Clinical Documentation Improvement." *Journal of AHIMA* 86, no. 7 (July): 46–50.

American Hospital Association (AHA). 2017. *Coding Clinic for ICD-10-CM and ICD-10-PCS*, 1st Quarter, 2017. https://www.codingclinicadvisor.com/downloadable-materials.

American Medical Association (AMA). 2022. *CPT Professional 2022*. Chicago: AMA.

American Society for Parenteral and Enteral Nutrition (ASPEN). 2021. "Clinical Guidelines." http://www.nutritioncare.org/Guidelines_and_Clinical_Resources/Clinical_Guidelines/.

Arora, R. D., and J. Boster. 2022. "Malignant Pleural Effusion." In *StatPearls* [Internet]. Treasure Island, FL: StatPearls Publishing. https://www.ncbi.nlm.nih.gov/books/NBK574541/.

Bolin-Deon, A., and L. Woodley. 2021. "Artificial Intelligence: What We Learned While Implementing CDI, CAC, and Scanning Software Solutions." *Journal of AHIMA*. May 11. https://journal.ahima.org/page/artificial-intelligence-what-we-learned-while-implementing-cdi-cac-and-scanning-software-solutions.

Bronnert, J. 2005. "Coding Ethically." *Journal of AHIMA* 76, no. 9: 108, 110, 112.

Buttner, P. 2015. "CPT Updates for CY 2015." *Journal of AHIMA* 86, no. 2: 62–64.

Casto, A. B. 2018. *Principles of Healthcare Reimbursement*, 6th ed. Chicago: AHIMA.

Casto, A. B., and S. White. 2021. *Principles of Healthcare Reimbursement and Revenue Cycle Management*, 7th ed. Chicago: AHIMA.

Centers for Disease Control and Prevention (CDC). 2010. "Ventilator-Assisted Pneumonia." Healthcare-Associated Infections. Last reviewed November 24, 2010. https://www.cdc.gov/hai/vap/vap.html.

Centers for Disease Control and Prevention (CDC). 2017. "Pneumocystis." https://www.cdc.gov/dpdx/pneumocystis/index.html.

Centers for Disease Control and Prevention (CDC). 2021. "Peripheral Arterial Disease (PAD)." Heart Disease. Last reviewed September 21, 2021. https://www.cdc.gov/heartdisease/PAD.htm.

Centers for Disease Control and Prevention (CDC). 2022. "About Stroke." Last reviewed November 22, 2022. https://www.cdc.gov/stroke/about.htm.

Centers for Disease Control and Prevention (CDC). 2022. "How Is Prostate Cancer Treated?" Last reviewed August 25, 2022. https://www.cdc.gov/cancer/prostate/basic_info/treatment.htm.

Centers for Medicare and Medicaid Services (CMS). 2011. "MLN Matters." Outreach-and-Education /Medicare-Learning-Network-MLN/MLNMattersArticles SE1237.pdf.

Centers for Medicare and Medicaid Services (CMS). 2013. "Hospital-Acquired Conditions." https://www.cms.gov/Medicare/Medicare-Fee-for-Service-Payment/HospitalAcqCond/Hospital-Acquired_Conditions.html.

Centers for Medicare and Medicaid Services (CMS). 2014a. "MLN Fact Sheet: Proper Use of Modifiers 59 & –X{EPSU}." Medicare Learning Network. https://www.cms.gov/files/document/mln1783722-proper-use-modifiers-59-xepsu.pdf.

Centers for Medicare and Medicaid Services (CMS). 2014b. "Transmittal: 1422; Change Request: 8863." https://www.cms.gov/Regulations-and-Guidance/Guidance/Transmittals/Downloads/R1422OTN.pdf.

Centers for Medicare and Medicaid Services (CMS). 2015a. "Evaluation and Management Services Guide. ICN: 006764.» Medicare Learning Network. https://www.cms.gov/Outreach-and-Education/Medicare-Learning-Network-MLN/MLNProducts/Downloads/eval-mgmt-serv-guide-ICN006764.pdf.

Centers for Medicare and Medicaid Services (CMS). 2015b. "Fact Sheet: Two-Midnight Rule." https://www.cms.gov/newsroom/fact-sheets/fact-sheet-two-midnight-rule-0.

Centers for Medicare and Medicaid Services (CMS). 2016a. "Appendix D: MS-DRG Tables." https://www.cms.gov/Medicare/Medicare-Fee-for-Service-Payment/AcuteInpatientPPS/Downloads/FY2016-CMS-1632-FR-MS-DRG.zip.

Centers for Medicare and Medicaid Services (CMS). 2016b. *ICD-10-CM/PCS MS-DRG v40.0 Definitions Manual*. https://www.cms.gov/icd10m/version39.0-fullcode-cms/fullcode_cms/P0001.html.

Centers for Medicare and Medicaid Services (CMS). 2016c. "Program Integrity: Self-Audit Snapshot." https://www.cms.gov/Medicare-Medicaid-Coordination/Fraud-Prevention/Medicaid-Integrity-Education/Downloads/ebulletins-self-audit.pdf.

Centers for Medicare and Medicaid Services (CMS). 2021. "Hospital-Acquired Conditions (Present on Admission Indicator)." Last updated December 21, 2021. https://www.cms.gov/Medicare/Medicare-Fee-for-Service-Payment/HospitalAcqCond.

Centers for Medicare and Medicaid Services (CMS). 2022a. "Coding." https://www.cms.gov/Medicare/Medicare-Fee-for-Service-Payment/HospitalAcqCond/Coding.

Centers for Medicare and Medicaid Services (CMS). 2022b. "FY 2022 IPPS Final Rule Homepage." https://www.cms.gov/medicare/acute-inpatient-pps/fy-2022-ipps-final-rule-home-page.

Centers for Medicare and Medicaid Services (CMS). 2022c. "Hospital-Acquired Condition Reduction Program." https://www.cms.gov/Medicare/Quality-Initiatives-Patient-Assessment-Instruments /Value-Based-Programs/HAC/Hospital-Acquired-Conditions.

Centers for Medicare and Medicaid Services (CMS). 2022d. "Medicare Fee for Service Recovery Audit Program." https://www.cms.gov/Research-Statistics-Data-and-Systems/Monitoring-Programs /Medicare-FFS-Compliance-Programs/Recovery-Audit-Program/.

Centers for Medicare and Medicaid Services (CMS). 2022e. "MS-DRG Classifications and Software." Last modified November 18, 2022. https://www.cms.gov/Medicare/Medicare-Fee-for-Service -Payment/AcuteInpatientPPS/MS-DRG-Classifications-and-Software.

Centers for Medicare and Medicaid Services (CMS). 2023a. *ICD-10-CM Official Guidelines for Coding and Reporting.* https://www.cms.gov/files/document/fy-2023-icd-10-cm-coding-guidelines.pdf.

Centers for Medicare and Medicaid Services (CMS). 2023b. *ICD-10-PCS Official Guidelines for Coding and Reporting.* https://www.cms.gov/medicare/icd-10/2023-icd-10-pcs.

Centers for Medicare and Medicaid Services Medicaid Code Editor. 2011. *Definitions of Medicare Code Edits.* https://www.cms.gov/medicare/coding/icd10/downloads/icd10_mce27_user_manual.pdf.

Code of Federal Regulations (CFR). 2022. "Medical Review Requirements." Title 42, Chapter IV, Subchapter B, Part 412, Subpart C, 42 CFR § 412.46. https://www.ecfr.gov/current/title-42/chapter -IV/subchapter-B/part-412/subpart-C/section-412.46.

Code of Federal Regulations (CFR). 2022. "Conditions of Participation for Hospitals." Title 42, Chapter IV, Subchapter G, Part 482. https://www.ecfr.gov/current/title-42/chapter-IV/subchapter-G/part-482.

Cook, A. M., G. Morgan Jones, G. W. J. Hawryluk, P. Mailloux, D. McLaughlin, A. Papangelou, S. Samuel . . . L. Shutter. 2020. "Guidelines for the Acute Treatment of Cerebral Edema in Neurocritical Care Patients." *Neurocritical Care* 32: 647–666. https://www.ncbi.nlm.nih.gov/pmc/articles /PMC7272487/.

Drugs.com. n.d. Home page. www.drugs.com.

Drugs.com. 2022. "Aspiration Pneumonia." Last update October 31, 2022. https://www.drugs.com/cg /aspiration-pneumonia.html.

Endicott, M. 2016. "Coding Sepsis vs. Septic Shock." *Journal of AHIMA* (website), April. https://library .ahima.org/doc?oid=301505#.Y3tre3bMKM9.

Fahrenholz, S., and R. Russo. 2013. *Documentation for Health Records.* Chicago: AHIMA.

Fenton, S., and S. Biedermann. 2014. *Introduction to Healthcare Informatics.* Chicago: AHIMA.

Foley, D. 2022. *CCS Exam Preparation*, 12th ed. Chicago: AHIMA.

Foltz, D. A., K. M. Lankisch, and N. B. Sayles. 2016. "Fraud and Abuse." In *Health Information Management Technology: An Applied Approach*, 5th ed., edited by N. B. Sayles and L. L. Gordon (Chapter 16). Chicago: AHIMA.

Garvin, J. 2015. *Certified Coding Specialist (CCS) Exam Preparation*, 6th ed. Chicago: AHIMA.

Giannangelo, K., ed. 2018. *Healthcare Code Sets, Clinical Terminologies, and Classification Systems*, 4th ed. Chicago: AHIMA.

Health Care Excel. 2003. Pneumonia (documentation suggestions). http://library.ahima.org /doc?oid=59750#.VzDtR4QrK73.

Hess, P. 2015. *Clinical Documentation Improvement: Principles and Practice.* Chicago: AHIMA.

Hess, P. 2018. *Clinical Documentation Improvement for Outpatient Care.* Chicago: AHIMA.

Jenkins, N. R. 2017. "Clinical Information and Nonclinical Data, Health Record Design." In *Documentation for Health Records*, 2nd ed., Chapter 5, edited by C. G. Fahrenholz. Chicago: AHIMA.

Johns, M. 2020. "Governing Data and Information Assets." In *Health Information Management: Concepts, Principles, and Practice*, 6th ed., Chapter 3, edited by P. K. Oachs and A. L. Watters. Chicago: AHIMA.

Kelly, J., and P. Greenstone. 2020. *Management of the Health Information Professional*, 2nd ed. Chicago: AHIMA.

Kuehn, L. M., and T. M. Jorwic. 2020. *ICD-10-PCS: An Applied Approach*. Chicago: AHIMA.

LaTour, K. M., S. Eichenwald Maki, and P. K. Oachs, eds. 2013. *Health Information Management: Concepts, Principles, and Practice,* 4th ed. Chicago: AHIMA.

Leon-Chisen, N. 2013. *ICD-10-CM and ICD-10-PCS Coding Handbook*. Chicago: American Hospital Association.

Leon-Chisen, N. 2022. *ICD-10-CM and ICD-10-PCS Coding Handbook 2022 with Answers*. Chicago: Health Forum.

MedlinePlus. n.d. "Albumin Blood Test." https://medlineplus.gov/lab-tests/albumin-blood-test/.

MedlinePlus. n.d. "Alcoholic liver disease." https://medlineplus.gov/ency/article/000281.htm.

MedlinePlus. n.d. "Heart Failure." https://medlineplus.gov/heartfailure.html.

MedlinePlus. n.d. "Jaundice." https://medlineplus.gov/ency/article/000210.htm

MedlinePlus. n.d. "Kidney Tests." https://medlineplus.gov/kidneytests.html.

MedlinePlus. n.d. "Pleural Effusion." https://medlineplus.gov/ency/article/000086.htm.

MedlinePlus. n.d. "Seizures." https://medlineplus.gov/seizures.html.

MedlinePlus. n.d. "Sepsis." https://medlineplus.gov/sepsis.html.

MedlinePlus. n.d. "Unstable Angina." https://medlineplus.gov/ency/article/000201.htm.

MedlinePlus. 2020. "Lactic Acid Test." https://medlineplus.gov/lab-tests/lactic-acid-test/.

Oachs, P., and A. Watters (eds.). 2020. *Health Information Management: Concepts, Principles, and Practice*, 6th ed. Chicago: AHIMA.

Office of Inspector General. 2016. *OIG Workplan*. US Department of Health and Human Services. http://oig.hhs.gov/reports-and-publications/workplan/index.asp.

Ojha, N., and A. S. Dhamoon. 2022. "Myocardial Infarction." *National Library of Medicine.* https://www.ncbi.nlm.nih.gov/books/NBK537076/.

Palkie, B. 2013. "Clinical Classifications and Terminologies." In *Health Information Management: Concepts, Principles and Practice*, 4th ed., Chapter 15, edited by K. M. LaTour, S. Eichenwald Maki, and P. Oachs. Chicago: AHIMA.

Reynolds, R. B., and A. Morey. 2020. "Heath Record Content and Documentation." In *Health Information Management: Concepts, Principles, and Practice*, 6th ed., Chapter 4, edited by P. Oachs and A. Watters. Chicago: AHIMA.

Rinehart-Thompson, L. A. 2017a. "HIPAA Privacy Rule: Part II." In *Fundamentals of Law for Health Informatics and Information Management*, 3rd ed., Chapter 11, edited by M. S. Brodnik, L. A. Rinehart-Thompson, and R. B. Reynolds. Chicago: AHIMA.

Rinehart-Thompson, L. A. 2017b. "Legal Health Record Maintenance, Content, Documentation, and Disposition." In *Fundamentals of Law for Health Informatics and Information Management*, 3rd ed., Chapter 9, edited by M. S. Brodnik, L. A. Rinehart-Thompson, and R. B. Reynolds. Chicago: AHIMA.

RxList.com. n.d. Home Page. https://www.rxlist.com/.

Sayles, N. B. 2020. "Health Information Functions, Purposes, and Users." In *Health Information Management Technology: An Applied Approach*, 6th ed., Chapter 3, edited by N. B. Sayles and L. L. Gordon. Chicago: AHIMA.

Schraffenberger, L., and L. Kuehn. 2011. *Effective Management of Coding Services*. Chicago: AHIMA.

Schraffenberger, L. A., and B. Palkie. 2020. *Basic ICD-10-CM and ICD-10-PCS Coding 2020*. Chicago: AHIMA.

Shaw, P., and D. Carter. 2020. *Registered Health Information Administrator (RHIA) Exam Preparation*, 9th ed. Chicago: AHIMA.

Shebl, E., V. S. Mirabile, A. Sankari, and B. Burns. 2022. "Respiratory Failure." *National Library of Medicine*. https://www.ncbi.nlm.nih.gov/books/NBK526127/.

Taghavi, S., A. Nassar, and R. Askari. 2022. "Hypovolemic Shock." In *StatPearls* [Internet]. Treasure Island, FL: StatPearls Publishing. https://pubmed.ncbi.nlm.nih.gov/30020669/.

Territo, M. 2022. "Neutropenia." *Merck Manual*. Last modified September 2022. https://www.merckmanuals.com/home/blood-disorders/white-blood-cell-disorders/neutropenia.

Townsend, H. 2013. "Natural Language Processing and Clinical Outcomes: The Promise and Progress of NLP for Improved Care." *Journal of AHIMA* 84, no. 2 (March): 44–45. https://library.ahima.org/doc?oid=106198#.Y0eom0zMJjs.

Wisconsin Health Information Management Association. 2022. "Practice Brief; Prospective Clinical Documentation Integrity (CDI) Reviews and Query/Alert Practice Best Standards. https://www.whima.org/practice-brief-prospective-cdi-reviews-and-query-alert-practice-best-standards/.